A2-Level

Biology

AQA A

The Revision Guide

Editor:
Kate Houghton.

Contributors:
Gloria Barnett, Ellen Bowness, Wendy Butler, Martin Chester, James Foster, Derek Harvey, Simon Little, Kate Redmond, Katherine Reed, Adrian Schmit, Rachel Selway, Emma Singleton, Jennifer Underwood.

Proofreader:
Vanessa Aris.

Published by Coordination Group Publications Ltd.

ISBN-10: 1 84146 394 9
ISBN-13: 978 1 84146 394 0
Groovy website: www.cgpbooks.co.uk
Jolly bits of clipart from CorelDRAW®
Printed by Elanders Hindson Ltd, Newcastle upon Tyne.

Contents

Meiosis

You might remember meiosis from AS — it's the one needed for sexual reproduction (no sniggering at the back, please).

Meiosis is a Special type of Cell Division

Meiosis **halves** the chromosome number. It's used for sexual reproduction in plants and animals.

In animals, meiosis produces the **gametes** (sperm and egg cells) and takes place in the **testes** and **ovaries**.
When the gametes fuse at **fertilisation** they combine their chromosomes, so the chromosome number is **restored**.
These two processes make sure that **chromosome numbers stay constant** overall from generation to generation.

Meiosis creates Haploid Cells

Meiosis has **two divisions**, and each one is made up of stages called **interphase**, **prophase**, **metaphase**, **anaphase** and **telophase**. The **first division** (parts 1-5 in the diagram) **halves** the chromosome number, and the **second division** (parts 6-11) **separates** the pairs of chromatids that make up each chromosome, like in **mitosis**.

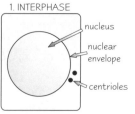

1. INTERPHASE

nucleus

nuclear envelope

centrioles

The cell is diploid
(it has two sets of chromosomes.)
It replicates its DNA, ready to divide.

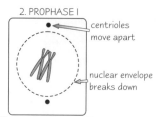

2. PROPHASE I

centrioles move apart

nuclear envelope breaks down

Chromatin coils up and becomes visible as chromosomes, each chromosome consisting of 2 chromatids. Homologous chromosomes pair up — the pairs are known as bivalents.

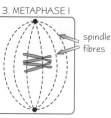

3. METAPHASE I

spindle fibres

Pairs of chromosomes go to the centre of the cell.

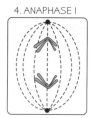

4. ANAPHASE I

Members of each homologous pair of chromosomes separate and are pulled apart along the spindle fibres.

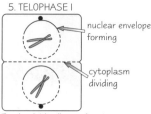

5. TELOPHASE I

nuclear envelope forming

cytoplasm dividing

Two haploid cells are forming.

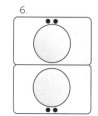

6.

This is the beginning of meiosis II. The cells prepare to divide again.

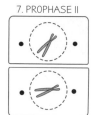

7. PROPHASE II

Chromosomes coil up once more. Each chromosome consists of 2 sister chromatids.

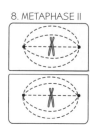

8. METAPHASE II

Chromosomes line up in centre of cells.

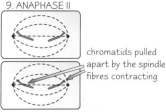

9. ANAPHASE II

chromatids pulled apart by the spindle fibres contracting

Each chromosome splits into its chromatids.

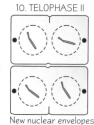

10. TELOPHASE II

New nuclear envelopes form. Cells divide.

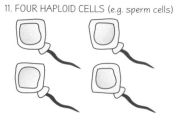

11. FOUR HAPLOID CELLS (e.g. sperm cells)

Haploid cells have only one set of chromosomes.

The diagram only shows what happens to one pair of chromosomes. In human cells, there are 23 pairs of chromosomes in total, all doing the same thing.

Cells divide Twice in Meiosis

First division (Meiosis I)

The chromosome pairs come together. The two chromosomes of a pair are called **homologous** chromosomes (see the next page). When they pair up, the pair is called a **bivalent**. Then, these homologous chromosomes move to opposite ends of the cell, and the cell divides. Now, there are **two haploid cells** instead of one diploid cell.

Second division (Meiosis II)

This is **similar** to **mitosis** (check in your AS notes if you can't remember).
Each new **haploid cell** divides, and each chromosome splits into its **chromatids**.

Meiosis

Crossing Over happens between Chromatids during Prophase I

During **prophase I**, the homologous chromosomes **exchange** pieces of their chromatids. This is called **crossing over.**

Crossing over happens randomly between the homologous chromosomes at any place along them.

The place where crossing over occurs is called a **chiasma** (plural: **chiasmata**). Crossing over helps to mix up alleles in new combinations and creates **variation**.

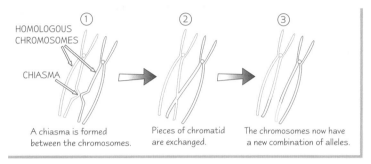

A chiasma is formed between the chromosomes.

Pieces of chromatid are exchanged.

The chromosomes now have a new combination of alleles.

You need to Learn some Key Terms

There's a lot of **fancy words** used about genetics and inheritance. Make sure you know these **important ones**:

chromosome	A strand of genetic material (DNA) found in the nucleus of a cell. Each chromosome consists of one molecule of DNA and histone proteins.
chromatid	One of the two identical strands of genetic material that make up a chromosome during cell division.
homologous	Homologous chromosomes are a pair of equivalent chromosomes with the same structure and arrangement of genes — usually one is inherited from the mother and one from the father.
bivalent	A pair of homologous chromosomes.
haploid	A cell with only half the number of chromosomes of the parent organism (only one copy of each chromosome), e.g. sperm and egg cells.
diploid	A cell with the full number of chromosomes — in pairs of homologous chromosomes.
gene	A section of DNA on a chromosome which controls a characteristic in an organism. It carries the genetic code to make one or more polypeptide or protein, or to make RNA.
locus	The position on a chromosome where a particular gene is located.
allele	An alternative form of a gene. E.g. in pea plants, the gene for height has two forms — one allele for tall plants and one allele for short plants.
genotype	The alleles a particular individual has.
phenotype	An individual's characteristics, e.g. eye colour, blood group.
homozygous	An individual with two copies of the same allele for a particular gene.
heterozygous	An individual with two different alleles for a particular gene.
dominant	The condition in which the effect of only one allele is apparent in the phenotype, even in the presence of an alternative allele.
codominance	The phenomenon in a heterozygote in which the effects of both alleles are apparent in the phenotype.
recessive	The condition in which the effect of an allele is apparent in the phenotype of a diploid organism only in the presence of another identical allele.
linked	Genes located on the same chromosome that are often inherited together.

Practice Questions

Q1   At which stage in meiosis: a) do the cells become haploid? b) does crossing-over occur?

Q2   Place these events in meiosis in the correct order: A. chromatids separate; B. homologous chromosomes pair up; C. two haploid cells are produced; D. homologous chromosomes separate; E. four haploid cells are produced.

Exam Questions

Q1   In which organs of the human body does meiosis occur?   [2 marks]

Q2   Explain the difference between: a) a gene and an allele; b) haploid and diploid.   [4 marks]

Q3   Explain the importance of meiosis in the life-cycles of sexually reproducing organisms.   [3 marks]

How do you tell the sex of a chromosome? Pull down its genes...

Remember that genes are carried on the chromosomes, so whatever the chromosomes do (like separating and re-combining), the genes will do too. It's a huge diagram, but just break it down into meiosis I and II, and learn the names of each phase, and what happens in each one. Use your AS notes to help you if you're still not sure.

Monohybrid and Dihybrid Crosses

Brace yourself for two pages of genetic diagrams. You need to get comfortable with these, because in the exam you'll not only have to interpret them, you might have to draw some of your own.

Monohybrid Inheritance Involves One Characteristic

Each individual has **two copies** of a gene. But they **segregate** when the sex cells are formed in meiosis, so each **gamete** contains only **one copy** of **every** gene. Monohybrid inheritance is the **simplest** form of inheritance — it's just inheritance where a single gene is being considered. A **monohybrid cross** is a genetic cross for only one gene:

<u>Example</u>

In fruit flies, the allele for **normal wings** is **dominant** (N), and the allele for **vestigial** (short) wings is **recessive** (n).

A normal-winged fruit fly is crossed with a fruit fly that has vestigial wings. **All** the offspring are normal-winged. These flies then **interbreed**, and the next generation shows a **3:1 ratio** of normal wings to vestigial wings, i.e. a 75% chance of normal wings and a 25% chance of vestigial wings.

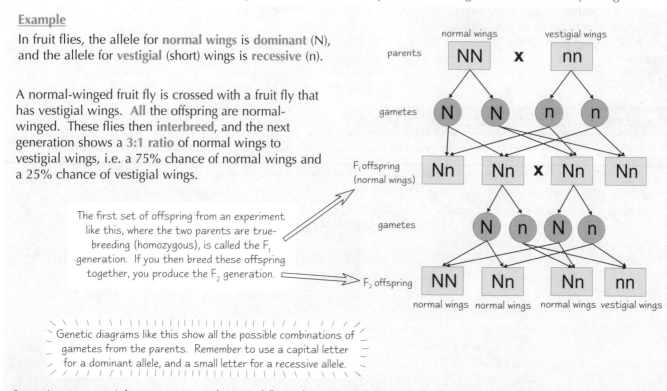

The first set of offspring from an experiment like this, where the two parents are true-breeding (homozygous), is called the F_1 generation. If you then breed these offspring together, you produce the F_2 generation.

Genetic diagrams like this show all the possible combinations of gametes from the parents. Remember to use a capital letter for a dominant allele, and a small letter for a recessive allele.

Sometimes, you might cross a normal-winged fly with a vestigial-winged fly and get a **1:1 ratio** of normal wings to vestigial wings in the offspring, instead of all normal. This happens if the normal-winged fly is **heterozygous** — it has **one allele** for **normal** wings, and **one allele** for **vestigial** wings. Because the allele for vestigial wings is recessive, it doesn't show up in the phenotype of heterozygous flies — vestigial wings is a recessive condition. The only way of telling a normal winged fly's genotype is by doing a **breeding experiment** called a **test cross** where you mate it with a recessive individual and see what the phenotypes of the offspring are — if any of them show **recessive** traits then you know that the parent that didn't show the trait must be a **carrier** of the gene (i.e. it is **heterozygous**).

Genes on Different Chromosomes Segregate Independently

Dihybrid inheritance shows how **two** different genes are inherited. Each gene gives a 3:1 ratio in the F_2 generation, but because the two genes do this **independently**, it makes a **9:3:3:1 ratio** overall. This diagram shows how this happens for two traits in the fruit fly.

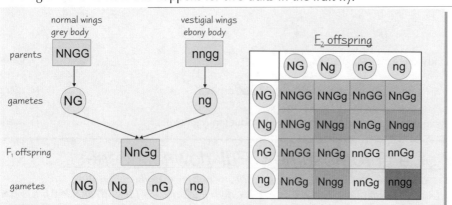

*Crossing an F_1 fly with a double recessive fly (vestigial wings and ebony body) gives a 1:1:1:1 **ratio**. Check your understanding by working this out yourself.*

Monohybrid and Dihybrid Crosses

In **Mammals** Sex is Determined by the **X** and **Y** Chromosomes

The genetic information for your **gender** is carried on two **specific** chromosomes:

1)   In mammals, **females** have **two X** chromosomes, and **males** have **one X** and **one Y**. The probability of having male or female offspring is **50%**.

2)   The Y chromosome is **smaller** than the X chromosome and carries **fewer genes**. So most genes carried on the sex chromosomes are only carried on the X chromosome. These genes are sex-linked. Males only have **one copy** of the genes on the X chromosome. This makes them more likely than females to show **recessive phenotypes**.

3)   Genetic disorders inherited this way include **colour-blindness** and **haemophilia**. The pattern of inheritance can show that the characteristic is **sex-linked**. In the example below, females would need **two copies** of the recessive allele to be colour blind, while males only need one copy.
This means colour blindness is **much rarer** in **women** than **men**.

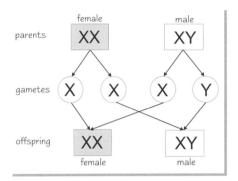

A carrier is a person carrying an allele which is not expressed in the phenotype, but which can be passed on.

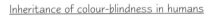

Inheritance of colour-blindness in humans

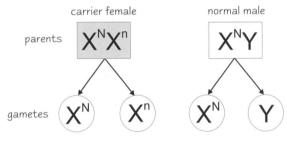

possible offspring

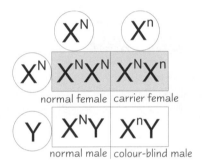

N = allele for normal eyesight
n = allele for colour-blindness

Practice Questions

Q1   What genetic ratios do you expect from each of these crosses?
a) Aa × Aa   b) AA × Aa   c) Aa × aa

Q2   What is the F_2 generation?

Q3   Explain why dihybrid crosses produce different ratios to monohybrid crosses.

Q4   Why is it rare for a woman to be colour-blind?

Q5   Name a sex-linked condition (other than colour-blindness).

Exam Question

Q1   In pea plants, the allele for purple flowers is dominant over the allele for white flowers.
How would you find out if a purple-flowered plant is homozygous or heterozygous?   [3 marks]

It's hard to do test crosses on humans...

If you're wondering whether you're heterozygous for a particular trait, it's probably not an option to breed with a recessive person, and then have lots of babies and see what they look like, unless you take your science homework very seriously.

Multiple Alleles and Codominance

If you've recently discovered that you've got a different blood group than both of your parents, read these pages before you go giving the milkman a hard time. Chances are it's all down to multiple alleles.

Some Genes have Multiple Alleles

Inheritance is more complicated when there are more than two alleles of the same gene — **multiple alleles**.
E.g. in the **ABO blood group system** there are **three alleles** for blood type:

I^O is the **recessive** allele for blood group O. I^A is the allele for blood group **A**. I^B is the allele for blood group **B**.

Alleles I^A and I^B are **codominant** (see below) — people with copies of **both** these alleles will have a **phenotype** that expresses **both** alleles, i.e. blood group **AB**. In the diagram below, if members of a couple who are both **heterozygous** for blood groups A and B have children, those children could have one of **four** different blood groups — A, B, O or AB.

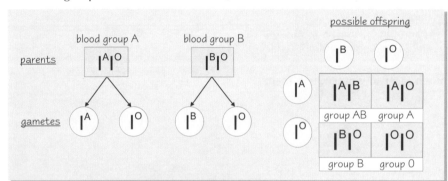

Recessive blood group alleles are normally really rare, but it just so happens that loads of people in Britain are descended from people who were $I^O I^O$, so it's really common.

Alleles can be Codominant

Occasionally, alleles show **codominance**. Codominance means that in **heterozygous** individuals the effects of both alleles are expressed in the phenotype.
One example in humans is the allele for **sickle-cell anaemia**:

- Normal people have two alleles for normal haemoglobin ($H_N H_N$).
- People with **sickle-cell anaemia** have two alleles for the disease ($H_S H_S$). Their red blood cells are sickle shaped, and can't carry oxygen properly. They usually die quite young.
- Heterozygous people ($H_N H_S$) have an in-between phenotype, called the **sickle-cell trait**. Some of their blood cells are normal, and some are sickle-shaped. The two alleles are **codominant**, because they're **both** expressed in the **phenotype**.

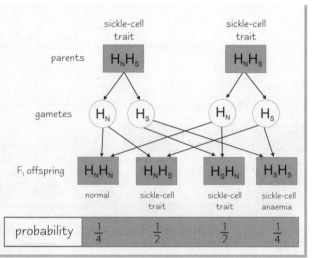

The Chi Square Test is Useful in Genetics

Look at the example about **dihybrid inheritance** in fruit flies on page 4. Suppose you actually did this cross as an experiment, using a sample of 160 flies in the F_2 generation — you'd be **expecting** to get an F_2 **ratio** of **9: 3: 3: 1**.
But it's pretty **unlikely** that you'd get that ratio **exactly**. Perhaps instead, out of 160 flies in the F_2 generation, you get:

81 flies with normal wings and a grey body.   26 flies with normal wings and an ebony body.
46 flies with vestigial wings and a grey body.   7 flies with vestigial wings and an ebony body.

That does look **a bit** like the expected 9: 3: 3: 1 ratio, but it's not **exactly** the same. You might guess that this difference is just due to **normal statistical chance**, but what if you're **wrong** and some other factor is affecting your results?
You can show whether or not this is likely to be true using a **statistical test** like the **chi square test**.

Multiple Alleles and Codominance

Use the Chi Square Test to check if Your Results match the Expected Results

The chi square test is used to test a **null hypothesis**. This will assume that there's **no statistically significant difference between sets of results** (e.g. between the results you'd **expect** to get in a genetic cross, and your **actual** results).
The chi square test checks whether any **difference** between the expected and the observed results is **significant** or not.

The **formula** you use to work out chi squared is:

$$\chi^2 = \sum \frac{(O-E)^2}{E}$$

Where:
O = observed result
E = expected result

You can only use your actual numbers when working out your result, not percentages. Oh, and don't panic — that equation will be provided in the exam.

The value you get is then looked up in a **chi square table** like the one on the right. You need to know the **degrees of freedom** to look up your result. This is just the number of categories (classes) **minus 1**. In the fruit fly experiment, there are **four** categories (normal and grey, normal and ebony, vestigial and grey, vestigial and ebony) so the degrees of freedom are 4 – 1 = **3**.

In the fruit fly example, out of 160 flies:

degrees of freedom	no. of classes	χ^2 values					
1	2	0.46	1.64	2.71	3.84	6.64	10.83
2	3	1.39	3.22	4.61	5.99	9.21	13.82
3	4	2.37	4.64	6.25	7.82	11.34	16.27
4	5	3.36	5.99	7.78	9.49	13.28	18.47
probability that deviation is due to chance alone		0.50 (50%)	0.20 (20%)	0.10 (10%)	0.05 (5%)	0.01 (1%)	0.001 (0.1%)

You **expected** to get:	What you **actually** got was:	Find **observed – expected** and **square it**:	
90 normal wings, grey body.	81 normal wings, grey body.	81 – 90 = -9	$-9^2 = 81$
30 normal wings, ebony body.	26 normal wings, ebony body.	26 – 30 = -4	$-4^2 = 16$
30 vestigial wings, grey body.	46 vestigial wings, grey body.	46 – 30 = 16	$16^2 = 256$
10 vestigial wings, ebony body.	7 vestigial wings, ebony body.	7 – 10 = -3	$-3^2 = 9$

Then **divide** each one by the **expected** result:

81 ÷ 90 =	0.9
16 ÷ 30 =	0.5
256 ÷ 30 =	8.5
9 ÷ 10 =	0.9

And **add them all together**:

0.9 + 0.5 + 8.5 + 0.9 = **10.8**

Looking this number up in the chi square table shows that it corresponds to a probability of between **0.05** and **0.01** that the deviation is due to **chance**. In the chi square test, the **critical value** is **p = 0.05**. This means that if the probability that the deviation is due to chance is **more** than p = 0.05 (i.e. a probability of more than **5%**), we can **accept the null hypothesis** that there is **no** statistically significant difference between the observed and the expected results.

In the case of our fruit flies, however, the probability is a bit **less** than 5%. So you have to **reject** the null hypothesis and say that there **is a statistically significant difference** between the results you got and the results you'd expected to get. Some **other factor** must be affecting the results, because the experiment has **not** obeyed the usual laws of inheritance.

Practice Questions

Q1   Do the genetics of the ABO blood group system show multiple alleles, codominance, or both?

Q2   What is sickle-cell anaemia? What type of inheritance pattern do sickle-cell alleles show?

Q3   What does the chi-squared test tell you about a set of results?

Q4   How do you know if the results of a chi-squared test are significant?

Exam Question

Q1   List the six possible genotypes for the human ABO blood groups.   [3 marks]

Q2   An experiment was carried out in which 10,000 people were tested for the disease sickle-cell anaemia in two different places. Place X is an African country with a high rate of malaria infection. Place Y is a temperate European country with a low rate of malaria infection. Explain how you could use the data from the experiment to find out if sickle-cell anaemia is more common in place X than place Y.   [2 marks]

Sickle-cell anaemia comes up all the time in exams

It's one of those examples that they like to put in all the time, so it's worth learning how codominance means that heterozygous people have some sickle-cells but their condition isn't as severe as homozygous people's.

Causes of Variation

Ever wondered why no two people are exactly alike? No, well nor have I, actually, but it's time to start thinking about it. This variation is partly genetic and partly due to differences in the environment.

Variation can be Continuous or Discontinuous

Discontinuous variation

This is when there are two or more **distinct types**, and each individual is one of these types, for example: **Sex** — you're either male or female. **Blood group** — you can be group A, group B, group AB or group O, but no intermediates.

Discontinuous variation has clear-cut categories because it depends on only one or a few genes (it is monogenic). So, there's a **limited number** of possible phenotypes. Discontinuous variation isn't so strongly influenced by the environment.

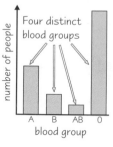

Continuous variation

This is when the individuals in a population vary along a **range**, with **no distinct types**, for example: **Height** — you could be any height over a range. **Weight** — you could be any weight over a range. **Skin colour** — any shade from very dark to very pale.

Continuous variation is **polygenic** — this means that several genes affect the same characteristic. Continuous variation can be more strongly affected by the **environment**. Because of the interaction of loads of different genes plus the effect of the environment, there's lots of possible phenotypes. For example, human body mass shows **continuous variation**. Your mass is **partly genetic** (big parents often have big children), but body mass is also strongly affected by **environmental factors** like diet and exercise.

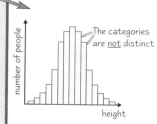

Genes and Environment interact in the Phenotype

Pea plants provide a clear example of the **interaction** between genes and environment that produces a **phenotype**.

Pea plants come in tall and dwarf forms.
This characteristic (tall or dwarf) is passed on from one generation to the next, so we can tell that it is **genetic**.

However, the tall plants vary in height, and so do the dwarf plants, so **environment** is involved too.

> Tall or dwarf is discontinuous variation. Height variation among the plants of each type is continuous variation.

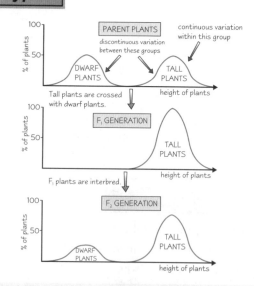

Studies of **twins** have been used to find out if a human characteristic is mainly influenced by **genes** or by **environment**. **Monozygotic** twins ("identical twins") have **identical genes** and **alleles**, because they both developed from the **same fertilised egg**. This means that if there are any differences in their characteristics, they may be due to the **environment**. Occasionally, monozygotic twins are raised **separately**, and comparing differences between them (compared with twins raised together) could show how important these environmental influences are.

Learn some examples where Environment affects the Phenotype

1) The **Himalayan rabbit** is mainly white, but some parts of its fur (at the ears, feet and tail) are black. The growth of the black fur is caused by environmental temperature — these parts of the body are cooler, and the black colour only develops when the skin temperature is below about 25 °C.

2) **Plant growth** is strongly affected by the environment — plants show better, healthier growth when there are more **nitrates** and other minerals available in the soil.

Causes of Variation

Sexual Reproduction helps create Variety

Sexual reproduction mixes up the alleles in new combinations, creating more **variety** in a species. This means that **survival** (of at least some individuals in a population) is more likely, so there's less chance of the species becoming extinct. If all individuals were the same, one set of environmental conditions or one disease could easily wipe them **all** out.

Sexual reproduction isn't the same as "sexual intercourse", or mating. It just means reproduction where two <u>gametes</u> (sex cells) <u>fuse</u> together to produce a new individual.

Meiosis creates new Chromosome Combinations

Meiosis (see pages 2-3) does more than just halve the chromosome number. It also helps create **genetic variety**, by producing new combinations of alleles. Here's how it happens:

Independent assortment of chromosomes

During **meiosis I**, the pairs of homologous chromosomes **separate** (at anaphase). The chromosomes from each pair end up **randomly** in one of the new cells, so you can get **different chromosome combinations**. In **meiosis II**, there's also random assortment of **chromatids**.

One pair of chromosomes would give **2** different types of haploid cell.

- Two pairs would give 2^2 possible haploid cells = **4 possibilities**.
- 23 pairs, like in humans, give 2^{23} possible haploid cells = over **8 million possibilities**. (Your parents would have to have millions of children before they stood any chance of having two genetically the same — unless they have twins.)

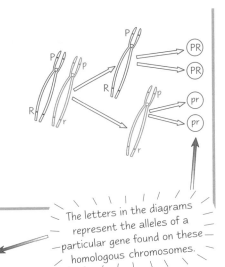

The letters in the diagrams represent the alleles of a particular gene found on these homologous chromosomes.

Crossing Over

Chromosomes often swap parts of their chromatids during **prophase I** (see page 2). This creates **new combinations** of alleles on those chromosomes, separating alleles that are normally inherited together (**linked**).

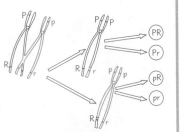

Mutation

Mistakes sometimes happen during cell division, producing a **completely new** characteristic (see page 12).

Meiosis also produces variation because it lets **fertilisation** take place. The **random fusion** of gametes from two individuals at fertilisation creates unique **combinations** of alleles.

Practice Questions

Q1 Give two examples of characteristics that show continuous variation, and two that show discontinuous variation.

Q2 Why it is important to have variety within a species?

Q3 State three ways in which meiosis helps to create variety within a species.

Exam Questions

Q1 If the body cells of an organism contain three pairs of chromosomes, how many different chromosome combinations can be produced in the gametes of this organism as a result of independent assortment? [2 marks]

Q2 Compare characteristics showing continuous and discontinuous variation with reference to:
a) the extent to which they are affected by the environment. [1 mark]
b) the number of genes that control them. [1 mark]

Variety is the spice of... meiosis...

By now you should have a pretty good idea of how meiosis creates variety in species. It's amazing to think of how many things influence the way that we look and behave. It's the reason we're all so lovely and unique... my parents often said they were glad they'd never have another child quite like me — I can't imagine why.

Investigating Variation

Apart from clones and identical twins no two organisms of the same species are genetically identical — there's always variation. These pages are all about measuring and analysing variation.

Sampling has to be **Random**

If you're sampling a small percentage of a population and then drawing conclusions about the whole population, it's important that the sample **accurately** represents the population **as a whole**.

One way to avoid bias in your answer is to pick the individuals in your sample **randomly**, e.g. you could number the individuals and then use a random number generator or table to choose your sample.

Once you have your data you've got to **Analyse It**

In a **normal distribution** of data, most of the samples are **close to the mean** (the average value), with relatively **few** samples at the **extremes**. On a graph, a normal distribution produces a **bell-shaped curve**, like the one below.

Standard deviation is often used to analyse data sets — it tells you how much a set of data is **spread out** around the **mean**.

The formula for standard deviation (s) is:

$$s = \sqrt{\dfrac{\sum x^2 - \dfrac{\left(\sum x \right)^2}{n}}{n-1}}$$

s is the standard deviation
$\sum$ means 'sum of'
x is an individual result
n is the total no. of results

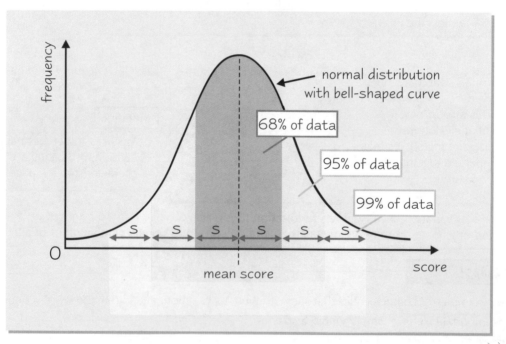

When all the samples have **similar** values then the distribution curve is **steep** and the standard deviation is **small**.

When the samples show a **lot** of **variation**, the distribution curve is relatively **flat** and there is a **large** standard deviation.

Investigating Variation

Standard Error tells you how accurate your Sample Mean is

1) If you take a **sample** of individuals from a whole population you can work out the **mean** for that sample. For example, you might find that in a sample of 25 the mean length of tadpoles in a pond is 11 mm.

2) If you took another sample of 25, you might find that the mean was 15 mm.

3) **Standard error** tells you how much **variation** in the **means** you are likely to get if you take **lots** of samples of the same size from a population.

4) A **big** standard error means there'll be **lots of variation** in the means and a **small** one means there **won't be much**.

5) You don't have to take lots of samples to work out the standard error, all you have to do is **divide** the s**tandard deviation** of the first set of data by the **square root** of the **number of observations**:

$$\frac{s}{\sqrt{n}}$$

where s is the standard deviation, and n is the number of observations in each sample.

This formula gives you a pretty good estimate of the standard error. (You'll get different estimates with different samples – but using one sample should give you a pretty good idea of the figure you're after.)

Practice Questions

Q1 What does standard deviation give an indication of?

Q2 In a normal distribution what percentage of the data lies within one standard deviation of the mean?

Q3 Name a set of data that you think might produce a normal distribution.

Q4 Explain what standard error tells you.

Exam Question

Q1 This graph shows the variation in the number of apples produced by different trees of the same species growing in the same orchard.

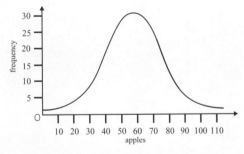

a) How can you tell from the graph that the variation in the number of apples is normally distributed? [1 mark]

b) Draw another curve on the graph to show what the distribution would look like if the standard deviation was much larger. [1 mark]

c) A new species of apple tree is developed by some scientists. When a test crop is grown the standard deviation of the data is very small. Suggest why farmers may prefer this new species to the one shown in the graph above. [2 marks]

Difficulty with statistics is a standard error...

The important thing is being able to interpret results. That means that you need to be able to tell the examiner what a standard deviation graph tells you about a set of data — remember that a large standard deviation means there's lots of variation. Make sure that you've got the hang of standard error too. Then run away and hide under a bush somewhere.

SECTION ONE — INHERITANCE AND EVOLUTION

Mutation and Phenotype

Mutation sounds quite exciting, but if you're expecting pictures of chickens with two heads or green monsters, you're going to be disappointed. Anyway, here's what happens when cell division goes wrong:

Point Mutations are Changes in the DNA Base Sequence

Before a cell divides, its DNA is replicated (copied) — look at your AS notes for more detail on DNA replication. Sometimes the base sequence of the DNA (the genetic code) gets changed. This is a **gene mutation** and it can make the DNA code for a different protein. A change of **one base** (C,G,A or T) is called a **point mutation**. The effect of a point mutation depends on exactly what happens:

No mutations

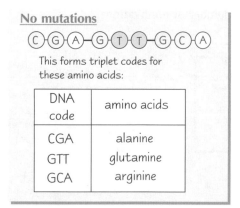

This forms triplet codes for these amino acids:

DNA code	amino acids
CGA	alanine
GTT	glutamine
GCA	arginine

Substitution

One base is **swapped** for another in a triplet code. It means that the gene will make a **similar protein** to the normal protein, but with just **one amino acid** different. Because the structure of a protein is so important, this can have a big effect. (The **sickle-cell** allele is the result of a base substitution.)

substitution here

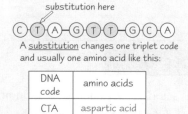

A <u>substitution</u> changes one triplet code and usually one amino acid like this:

DNA code	amino acids
CTA	aspartic acid
GTT	glutamine
GCA	arginine

Insertion (addition)

An **extra** nucleotide (with a base) is included in the DNA molecule. This has a much bigger effect than a substitution, because it causes **all** the following triplet codes in the gene to be altered. If there's an insertion, the gene doesn't make **any** useful protein at all, which can cause serious problems.

insertion here

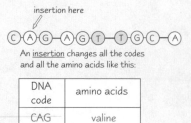

An <u>insertion</u> changes all the codes and all the amino acids like this:

DNA code	amino acids
CAG	valine
AGT	serine
TGC	threonine

Deletion

A nucleotide (with its base) is **missed** out when the DNA is copied. Like insertion, this **shifts along** all the triplet codes after it, so it really messes things up. This is also known as a '**frame shift**' mutation.

deletion here

C—A—G—T—T—G—C—A—T

A <u>deletion</u> changes all the codes and all the amino acids like this:

DNA code	amino acids
CAG	valine
TTG	asparagine
CAT	valine

Mutation and Phenotype

Mutagens make Mutations more likely

Mutations are accidents, and can happen for no obvious reason.
However **mutagens** make mutations more likely to happen:

1) **Radiation**

Some types of **radiation** are mutagenic. This includes X-rays, UV rays and ionising radiation such as gamma-rays.

2) **Chemicals**

Some **chemicals** are mutagens. Most of these chemicals are also carcinogens (they cause cancer).
E.g. mustard gas, and substances in tobacco smoke. These chemicals cause **point mutations** in the DNA.

Other chemical mutagens affect the structure of **chromosomes**, making chromosome mutation more likely.
E.g. the dye **colchicine** has this effect, and is used by **plant breeders** to produce new plant species.

Mutations are often Harmful

Any random change to the DNA in a cell is probably going to be **damaging**.
Most **genetic diseases** are the result of mutations.

Changes in the cell's DNA might mean that it codes for a different protein,
or for none at all, which could stop an important process from working.

> **The Human Genome Project (HGP)**
>
> This international project to **map the positions** of different genes on the chromosomes was completed in 2003.
>
> Information from the HGP will help scientists understand **mutations** and **genetic diseases**.

Albino wallaby Mervyn gets upset when people call him a mutant.

Mutations can lead to Evolution

Occasionally a mutation creates an **improvement**. If so, the mutant will have a selective advantage and will probably end up having more offspring, so **natural selection** causes the mutant form to become more common.
This type of mutation is important in **evolution**.

Practice Questions

Q1   Name the three main types of gene mutation.
Q2   Explain the difference between insertion and deletion.
Q3   Give examples of two chemical mutagens.

Exam Questions

Q1   Explain why the deletion of three adjacent nucleotides in a gene mutation will usually have a less severe
     effect on the phenotype than the deletion of one nucleotide.   [4 marks]

Q2   Suggest explanations for these facts:
     a) Radiographers in hospitals stay behind a lead screen when giving X-rays to patients.   [2 marks]
     b) Excessive exposure to bright sunlight can cause skin cancer.   [2 marks]
     c) When fruit-flies are exposed to X-rays, and then mated, some of their offspring have abnormal
        white eyes or deformed wings.   [2 marks]

So you're telling me I'm a mutant…

Loads of genetic diseases start off as just a random mutation in one person, then the mistake just keeps getting passed on down the generations. On the other hand, a mutation could be the reason for your stunning good looks.

Frequency of Alleles

Sometimes you need to look at the genetics of a whole population, rather than a cross between just two individuals. Here goes — get ready for a bit of statistics.

Members of a Population share a Gene Pool

A **population** is a group of organisms of the same species living in a particular area. The **gene pool** is all the genes and alleles present in the population.

The Hardy-Weinberg Principle can Predict Allele Frequency

You can use the **Hardy-Weinberg Principle** to work out the **frequency** of certain genotypes and phenotypes in a population. The principle can be demonstrated using the following example:

A species of plant has either **red** or **white** flowers. The frequency of the allele for a red flower (**A**) or a white flower (**a**) is written as a decimal between 0 and 1. So if the alleles for red and white flowers are **equally common**, they would each have a frequency of **0.5**.

In the **Hardy-Weinberg equation**:
p = the frequency of the dominant allele (A)
q = the frequency of the recessive allele (a)
If there are just two alleles for a gene, $p + q$ should $= 1$

Now you can work out the genotype frequencies:

p^2 = frequency of the genotype AA $2pq$ = frequency of the genotype Aa q^2 = frequency of the genotype aa

Every member of the population must have **one** of these genotypes, so: $p^2 + 2pq + q^2 = 1$.

Example

p (the frequency of allele A) is **0.8**, and q (the frequency of a) is **0.2**.
Work out the frequencies of the different **genotypes** (and **phenotypes**) in the population:

Frequency of AA = 0.8^2 = 0.64
Frequency of Aa = $2 \times 0.8 \times 0.2$ = 0.32 ← *These frequencies need to add up to 1.*
Frequency of aa = 0.2^2 = 0.04

You can **reverse** the equation — if you know the **phenotype frequencies** you can work out the **genotype** and **gene frequencies**:

Example

The frequency of cystic fibrosis in the UK is approximately **1 birth in 2000**.
Cystic fibrosis is caused by a **recessive allele**, so:
q^2 = 1/2000 = 0.0005
∴ $q = \sqrt{0.0005}$ = 0.0224 — this is the frequency of the cystic fibrosis allele.
∴ p = 1 - 0.0224 = 0.9776 — this is the frequency of the normal allele.
The proportion of the population who are **carriers** of the cystic fibrosis allele is $2pq = 2 \times 0.9776 \times 0.0005 = \underline{0.0438}$, so **4.38%** of the UK population carry the CF allele.

The Hardy-Weinberg Principle only works under Certain Conditions

The Hardy-Weinberg principle only applies in certain conditions:
- A **large population**.
- **Random mating** — all genotypes must be equally likely to mate with all others.
- No **immigration or emigration**.
- No **mutations** or **natural selection**.

This is because the Hardy-Weinberg principle relies on the **proportions** of the alleles of a particular gene staying **constant** from one generation to the next. If any of these conditions **aren't** met, it'll cause the **allele frequencies** in the population to start **changing**.

Frequency of Alleles

Selection affects Allele Frequencies

Selection can have **different effects** on a population:

1) **Stabilising** selection is where individuals with traits towards the **middle** of the range are more likely to survive and reproduce. It's the **commonest** type, which occurs when the environment is **not** changing. It helps to keep the population **stable**.

2) **Directional** selection is where individuals of **one extreme type** are more likely to survive and reproduce. This happens when the environment changes, and it causes corresponding **genetic change** in the population.

3) **Disruptive** selection is where **two different extreme types** are selected for, perhaps because they live in **two different habitats**. This leads to **two distinct types** developing, and eventually these may become **different species**.

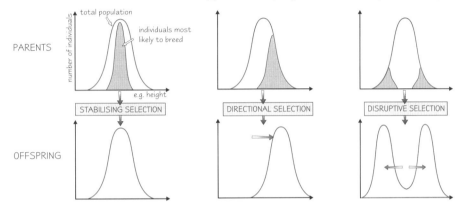

Selection depends on the Environment

Certain traits only become more **common** in a population because they give individuals a better chance of **surviving** and **reproducing** in the particular environmental **conditions** at the time.

Example

Sickle-cell anaemia is a genetic disorder common in tropical countries where malaria is endemic. People with **two copies** of the allele die quite young if they're not receiving treatment. One copy of the **sickle-cell allele** gives carriers some **protection** against malaria. In **non-malarial** parts of the world, the allele would be removed by **selection**, but in malarial areas it gives carriers an advantage so it stays in the population.

When the environment **changes**, so do the selection pressures. Over the past century, **humans** have started using **antibiotics** against bacteria, and insecticides against agricultural pests. Many populations of bacteria are becoming resistant to antibiotics, and pesticides are becoming less effective against the pests. These changes are the result of **directional selection**.

Practice Questions

Q1 What is the Hardy-Weinberg equation?

Q2 Explain three different conditions needed, if the Hardy-Weinberg Principle is to hold true.

Q3 Name the three different types of selection, and explain what effect each has on allele frequencies.

Exam Questions

Q1 In one of the human blood group systems, there are three blood groups, dependent on a single pair of codominant alleles. The genotypes and phenotypes are as follows: genotype MM - blood group M, genotype NN - blood group N, genotype MN - blood group MN. If the frequency of blood group M in a population is 0.36, use the Hardy-Weinberg equation to work out the frequencies of blood groups MN and N. [4 marks]

Q2 If malaria were eradicated from the world, explain what you'd expect to happen to the frequencies of the sickle-cell and normal alleles in the human population. What type of selection would cause the changes? [4 marks]

The best kind of selection comes in a box at Christmas...

The Hardy-Weinberg Principle looks a lot worse than it is, so don't be put off by the calculations. Like most equations in Biology, all you have to do is stick the figures that you have into the equation, then it's just simple maths.

Speciation

Speciation is all about how new species appear — there are two kinds of speciation that you need to know about — allopatric speciation and sympatric speciation.

Speciation *is the Development of a* **New Species**

A **species** is defined as a group of organisms that can **reproduce** and produce **fertile young**.
Every true species we know of has been named using the **binomial system** (see page 19).
When new species are discovered they are also classified using this system.

Sometimes two individuals from different species can breed and produce offspring. These **hybrid** offspring aren't a new species because they're **infertile**. For example, **lions** and **tigers** have bred together in zoos to produce **tigons** and **ligers** but they aren't new species because they **can't** produce offspring.

Speciation (development of a new species) happens when **populations** of the **same species** become **isolated**.
Local interbreeding populations of a species are called **demes** (be careful with this — demes aren't always isolated).

Geographical Isolation *causes* **Allopatric** *Speciation*

1) Geographical isolation happens when a **physical** barrier (e.g. mountains) **divides** a population of a species.

2) **Floods**, **volcanic eruptions** and **earthquakes** can all cause barriers that mean some individuals become **isolated** from the main population.

3) **Conditions** on either side of the barrier will be slightly **different**. For example, there might be a different **climate** on either side of the barrier.

4) Environmental conditions like this put **pressure** on the organisms, forcing them to **adapt** — the **natural selection processes** differ in each isolated group.

5) **Mutations** will take place **independently** in each population and, over a **long** period of time, the gene pools will **diverge** and the **allele frequencies** will **change**.

6) Eventually, individuals from different populations will have changed so much that they won't be able to breed with one another to produce **fertile** offspring — they'll have become **two separate species**.

 = individual organism

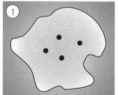 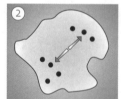 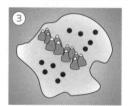 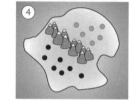

Population of individuals ⟹ Populations separate. ⟹ Physical barriers stop interbreeding between populations. ⟹ Populations adapt to new environments. ⟹ Gene pools diverge, leading to development of new species.

Sympatric Speciation *happens due to* **Reproductive Isolation**

Reproductive isolation happens when something **prevents** some members of a population breeding with each other. There are **several causes** of reproductive isolation:

1) **Seasonal isolation** — where a mutation or genetic drift means that some individuals of the same species have different **flowering** or **mating** seasons, or become **sexually active** at different times of the year.

2) **Mechanical isolation** — where mutations cause changes in genitalia which prevent successful mating.

3) **Behavioural isolation** where a group of individuals develop **courtship rituals** which are **not attractive** to the main population of a species.

4) **Gametic isolation** — where mutations mean that male and female **gametes** from different populations of the same species are **not** able to create new individuals — so the individuals can mate, but fertilisation fails or the foetus is aborted.

> If two populations have become so different that they can't breed then a **new species** will have been created — this is called **sympatric speciation**.

Speciation

Darwin's Finches are a good example of Allopatric Speciation

Darwin studied **finches** that live on the Galápagos Islands, a small group of islands 1000 km west of Ecuador, to develop his theory of evolution. He based his theory on his observations:

1) On the Galápagos islands, there are **fourteen** species of **finch** belonging to **four genera**.

2) Each species of finch inhabits a different ecological niche (see p. 20) on the islands and some are only found on one island.

3) The main difference between the finches is the **shape** and **size** of their **beaks**. The birds feed on a variety of different foods from grubs to hard-shelled seeds — each finch has a beak suited to the food it eats.

main food	fruits	large insects	insects	cacti	seeds	large seeds
feeding adaptation	parrot-like beak	grasping beak	uses cactus spines	large crushing beak	pointed crushing beak	large crushing beak

Despite these differences, Darwin thought that all the finches had a **common ancestor** (this is called **divergent** evolution). Since then more research has been done which has proved that **geographical isolation** did cause **speciation** on the Galápagos islands. Finches are small birds and it's unusual for them to fly over water, so once a population gets onto an island (perhaps because they were blown off course by a storm) they are effectively **isolated** from the finches on other islands. The differing environmental conditions on each island put **selection pressures** on the birds — and the birds gradually became **adapted** by natural selection to the conditions on the different islands.

Convergent Evolution is when Unrelated Species have Similar Features

Convergent evolution happens when **unrelated** species have **evolved** so that they look very **similar**. For example, **sharks** and **dolphins** look pretty similar and swim in a similar way but they're totally different species — sharks are cartilaginous **fish** and dolphins are **mammals**. They have different evolutionary roots but they have developed similar bone structures to make them well **adapted** for swimming.

Practice Questions

Q1 Define the term 'species'.

Q2 What is a hybrid? Give an example.

Q3 What is the difference between allopatric and sympatric speciation?

Q4 Name four causes of sympatric speciation.

Q5 What was Darwin researching when he proposed his theory of evolution?

Exam Question

Q1 Charles Darwin studied different species of finch on the Galápagos Islands.
a) Describe Darwin's observations. [3 marks]
b) Give an explanation of how Darwin believed the different species developed. [4 marks]

I wish there were biology field trips to the Galápagos Islands...

It's easy to learn the basics of these pages — what a species is and how new ones develop. Then it's just a matter of learning the detail and the correct words for everything. It's important that you know words like 'sympatric' and 'convergent evolution' because they might be used in the exam questions and you'll be stuck if you forget what they mean.

Classification and Taxonomy

Classification is all about grouping together organisms that have similar characteristics.
The system of classification in use today was invented by a Swedish botanist, Carolus Linnaeus, in the 1700s.

Classification *is the way Living Organisms are Divided into* **Groups**

The classification system in use today puts organisms into one of five **kingdoms**:

KINGDOM	EXAMPLES	FEATURES
Prokaryotae	bacteria	unicellular, no nucleus, less than 5 μm, naked DNA in circular strands, cell walls of peptidoglycan
Protoctista	algae, protozoa	eukaryotic cells, usually live in water, unicellular or simple multicellular
Fungi	moulds, yeasts and mushrooms	eukaryotic, heterotrophic, chitin cell wall, saprotrophic
Plantae	mosses, ferns, flowering plants	eukaryotic, multicellular, cell walls made of cellulose, photosynthetic, contain chlorophyll, autotrophic
Animalia	nematodes (roundworms), molluscs, insects, fish, reptiles, birds, mammals	eukaryotic, multicellular, no cell walls, heterotrophic

You can **Classify Organisms** *according to how they* **Feed**

There are **three** main ways of getting **nutrition** —

1) **Saprotrophic** organisms, e.g. **fungi**, absorb substances from **dead** or **decaying** organisms using **enzymes**.
2) **Autotrophic** organisms, e.g. **plants**, produce their **own** food using **photosynthesis**.
3) **Heterotrophic** organisms, e.g. **animals**, consume complex organic molecules, i.e they consume **plants** and **animals**.

All Organisms can be organised into **Taxonomic Groups**

Taxonomy is the branch of science that deals with **classification**.

A **species** is the **smallest** unit of classification (see p. 16-17 for more about species). Closely related species are grouped into **genera** (singular = genus) and closely related genera are grouped into **families**. The system continues like this in a hierarchical pattern until you get to the largest unit of classification, the **kingdom**.

The Hierarchy of Classification
Kingdom
Phylum
Class
Order
Family
Genus
Species

For Example, Humans are **Homo sapiens**

This is how **humans** are classified:

		FEATURES
KINGDOM	Animalia	animal
PHYLUM	Chordata	has nerve cord
CLASS	Mammalia	has mammary glands and feeds young on milk, has hair / fur
ORDER	Primates	finger and toe nails, opposable thumb, reduced snout and flattened face, binocular vision, forward-facing eyes
FAMILY	Hominidae	relatively large brain, no tail, skeleton adapted for upright or semi-upright stance
GENUS	*Homo*	cranial capacity > 750 cm³, upright posture
SPECIES	*sapiens*	erect body carriage, highly developed brain, capacity for abstract reasoning and speech

This column shows the features that have been used to classify humans into each of these groups.

Classification and Taxonomy

The **Binomial System** is used to **Name** organisms

The full name of a human is **Animalia Chordata Mammalia Primate Hominidae** *Homo sapiens*. The name gives you a lot of information about how humans have been classified. Using full names is a bit of a mouthful so it's common practice to just give the **genus** and **species** names — that's the **binomial** ('two names') **system**.

The binomial system has a couple of **conventions**:

1)   Names are always written in *italics* (or they're <u>underlined</u> if they're **handwritten**).

2)   The **genus** name is always **capitalised** and the **species** name always starts with a **lower case** letter.

e.g.

Human	*Homo sapiens*
Polar bear	*Ursus maritimus*
Sweet pea	*Lathyrus odoratus*

Cladograms show **Evolutionary Relationships**

When taxonomy was first developed organisms were classified according to characteristics that were **easy to observe**, for example, number of legs. Thanks to modern **scientific techniques** like **DNA technology**, **genetics**, **biochemical analysis** and **behavioural analysis**, many more **criteria** can now be used to classify organisms.

A **cladogram** is a diagram which emphasises **phylogeny** (the genetic relationship between organisms). Cladistics focuses on the features of organisms that are **evolutionary developments**. The **advantage** of cladograms is that you can see points where **one** species split into **two**.

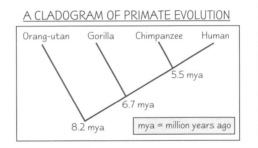

A CLADOGRAM OF PRIMATE EVOLUTION

Orang-utan   Gorilla   Chimpanzee   Human

5.5 mya

6.7 mya

8.2 mya   mya = million years ago

99.4% of a chimp's DNA is identical to human DNA. The fact that humans and chimps diverged most recently shows that humans are more closely related to chimps than they are to the other ape species in the cladogram.

Practice Questions

Q1   Name the five kingdoms of classification, giving an example organism in each.
Q2   What do the phrases saprotrophic, autotrophic and heterotrophic mean?
Q3   Explain the difference between fungi and plants in terms of how they get their nutrition.
Q4   What are the two rules for using the binomial system?

Exam Questions

Q1   Explain the difference between phylogenetic classification and traditional classification.   [2 marks]

Q2   The King Penguin has the scientific name *Aptenodytes patagonicus*.   [5 marks]
Fill out the missing words a) – e) in the table.

Kingdom	Animalia
a)	Chordata
b)	Aves
Order	Sphenisciformes
c)	Spheniscidae
Genus	d)
Species	e)

I prefer scantilycladograms...

The good thing about this is everything is pretty straightforward — don't be put off if lots of the words are new to you (and if 'cladogram' is part of your day-to-day vocabulary then I suggest you get out more). You need to learn this thoroughly. In the exam you'll be glad that you did cos there's often some easy marks to be had about this kind of stuff.

Energy Transfer in Ecosystems

These two pages deal with loads of words that you need to know. They also deal with the way energy flows through ecosystems. Not too difficult, but you need to understand the basic principles.

You need to learn some **Definitions** to get you started

Ecosystem	An **ecological unit** which includes all the **organisms** living in a particular area and all the **abiotic** (non-living) features of the local environment.
Population	All the **individuals** of a particular **species** living in a given area.
Community	All the **living organisms** in an ecosystem. These organisms are all **interconnected** by food chains and food webs.
Habitat	The **place** where the communities live, e.g. a rocky shore, a field, etc.
Niche	The **'role'** an organism has in its environment — where it lives, what it eats, where and when it feeds, when it is active etc. Every species has its own **unique** niche.
Environment	The **conditions** surrounding an organism, including both abiotic factors (e.g. temperature, rainfall) and biotic factors (e.g. predation, competition).

The opposite of abiotic is biotic (to do with living things).

Don't get confused between population size (how many in total), and density (how many in a given area).

Energy and **Nutrients Flow Through** ecosystems

Energy comes into the ecosystem from sunlight and is fixed into the ecosystem by plants during **photosynthesis**. The energy stored in the plants can then be passed onto other organisms in the ecosystem along **food chains** — each link in a food chain is called a **trophic level**. During this process a lot of the energy is gradually lost from the food chain — this is **dissipation**. **Nutrients** like nitrogen and potassium are passed from one organism to another too (see p22-23 for more on nutrient cycles).

All the food chains in an **ecosystem** are linked together in **food webs**.

Scientists call food chains and webs dynamic feeding relationships.

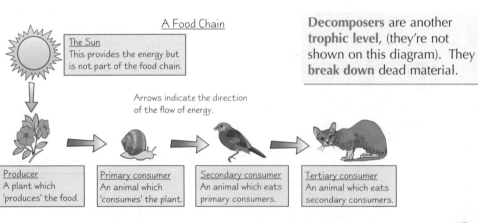

A Food Chain

The Sun
This provides the energy but is not part of the food chain.

Decomposers are another **trophic level**, (they're not shown on this diagram). They **break down** dead material.

Arrows indicate the direction of the flow of energy.

Producer
A plant which 'produces' the food.

Primary consumer
An animal which 'consumes' the plant.

Secondary consumer
An animal which eats primary consumers.

Tertiary consumer
An animal which eats secondary consumers.

1) At each trophic level about **10%** of the energy is used for **growth** and **storage** — that's the energy that can be passed onto the **next** level when the organism is **consumed**.

2) So about **90%** of energy is **wasted** between one trophic level and the next. The cow diagram shows what typically happens to this energy.

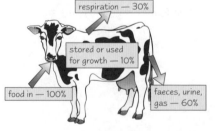

respiration — 30%

stored or used for growth — 10%

food in — 100%

faeces, urine, gas — 60%

All this wastage means that food chains rarely get longer than five links.

Energy Transfer in Ecosystems

Food chains can be shown as Three Types of Pyramid

In all food pyramids the **area** of each block tells you about the **size** of the trophic level.
The food chain can be shown in terms of number, biomass or energy:

Pyramids of Number

These are the **easiest to produce** — they show the **numbers** of the different organisms so it's just a question of counting.
They're **sometimes misleading**, though — the nice pyramid shape is often messed up by the presence of small numbers of big organisms (like trees) or large numbers of small organisms (like parasites).

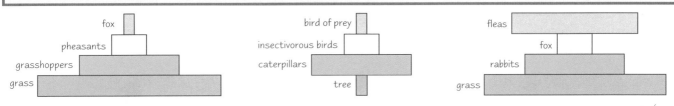

Pyramids of Biomass

These are produced by measuring biomass (the **dry mass** of the organisms in kg/m²).
It's **difficult to get the raw data** for them (you'd have to kill the organisms) but they're pretty accurate — they nearly always come out pyramid shaped.

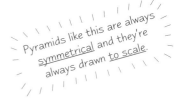

Pyramids like this are always symmetrical and they're always drawn to scale.

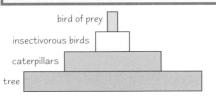

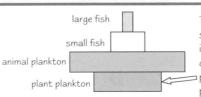

The amount of plant plankton is quite small at any given instant, but, because it has a short life and reproduces very quickly, there is a lot of it around over a period of time. This is why the plant plankton level is smaller than the animal plankton level.

Pyramids of Energy

These measure the **amount of energy** in the organisms in **kilojoules** per **square metre** per **year** ($kJm^{-2}yr^{-1}$).
This data is **very difficult to measure** but these pyramids give the **best picture of the food chain** and are **always proper pyramids**.

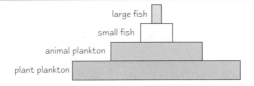

Practice Questions

Q1 What is a community?
Q2 What is a trophic level?
Q3 Why are there very rarely more than five links in a food chain?
Q4 What are the three types of pyramid?

Exam Questions

Q1 Explain the differences between a habitat and an ecosystem. [4 marks]

Q2 Pyramids of number and pyramids of biomass are not always pyramid-shaped, but pyramids of energy are.
     Explain why this is so. [4 marks]

Ah... pretty coloured pyramids — after section 1, this is pure heaven...

This stuff is fairly straightforward but there are quite a few definitions you need to get in your head before the rest of the section. Otherwise, come the harder stuff, you'll be struggling to remember what ecosystems, populations, communities and habitats are. Make sure you know how energy flows through ecosystems and the different types of pyramid as well.

Carbon and Nitrogen Cycles

The amount of carbon, nitrogen and oxygen on Earth is fixed — they can exist in different forms but no more can be made. The good news is they are constantly cycled around so they won't run out. The bad news is that you have to learn how that happens — just like you did for GCSE — only this time it's a bit more complicated. Great.

The **Carbon Cycle** is fairly straightforward

The carbon cycle involves four basic processes – **photosynthesis**, **respiration**, **death and decay** and **combustion**.

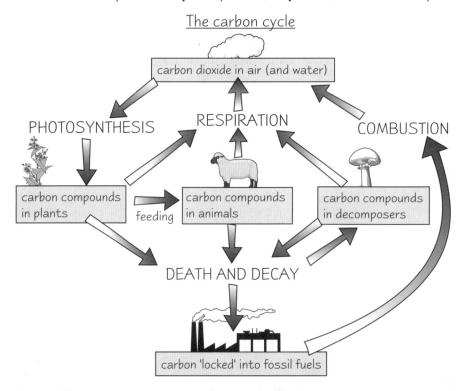

The carbon cycle

These are the seven things that you need to **remember** about the carbon cycle:

1) The only way that carbon gets into ecosystems is through **photosynthesis**.

2) Herbivores get their carbon by eating **plants**, carnivores get theirs by eating **other animals** and omnivores eat a **mixture** of plants and animals.

3) **Decomposers** get their carbon by digesting dead organisms. Feeding on dead material is **saprobiontic** or **saprotrophic nutrition**.

4) All living organisms return carbon to the air in the form of **carbon dioxide** through **respiration**.

5) If plants or animals **die** in situations where there are no decomposers (e.g. deep oceans) the carbon in them can get turned into **fossil fuels** over millions of years.

6) The carbon in fossil fuels is released when they are burned — **combustion**.

7) **Microorganisms** are important in the cycle because they can quickly get the carbon in dead material **back into the atmosphere**.

The **Carbon Cycle** keeps atmospheric carbon dioxide levels **Constant**

In a totally **natural** situation the carbon cycle would keep atmospheric levels of carbon dioxide **more or less the same**. Nowadays people are affecting the **global carbon balance** in two key ways:

- We burn huge quantities of **wood** and **fossil fuels** each year, which **adds** loads of carbon dioxide to the air.

- We are **clearing large areas of forest**, which would normally help to absorb some of the carbon dioxide in the atmosphere.

- In combination these two activities mean that the total amount of carbon in the atmosphere is much **higher** than it naturally would be.

Carbon and Nitrogen Cycles

The Nitrogen Cycle is a bit more Complicated

You need to be familiar with all the stages in the nitrogen cycle:

Don't worry if you get a diagram that looks different to this in the exam - all the information will be basically the same.

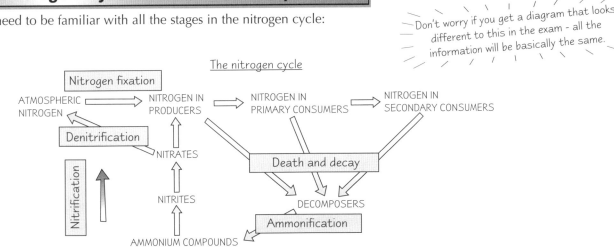

The nitrogen cycle

Plants and animals need nitrogen for **proteins** and for nucleic acids, but despite the atmosphere being 78% nitrogen, neither of them can use nitrogen gas. The key thing you need to remember is how important **bacteria** are (see box below). Without bacteria to produce the **nitrates** that plant roots can absorb, plants and animals couldn't exist.

1) Atmospheric nitrogen is **fixed** by **bacteria**. Some **live free** in the soil, others are found inside root nodules of **leguminous** plants (that's peas, beans and clover to you and me). Atmospheric nitrogen is changed into **ammonia**, then nitrites, then nitrates, which all plants can absorb and use to make protein.

2) The nitrogen in the plant proteins is passed onto animals through **food chains**.

3) When living organisms **die** their nitrogen is **returned** to the soil in the form of **ammonium compounds** by **microorganisms**. Animals get rid of excess amino acids via **deamination** in their livers — the nitrogen gets back into the soil via their **urine**.

4) Ammonium compounds are changed into nitrates by **nitrifying bacteria**. Firstly ammonium compounds are turned into nitrites, then the compounds are changed into nitrates.

5) Nitrates are **converted back** into atmospheric nitrogen by **denitrifying bacteria**.

Sometimes you'll see a couple of extra things on diagrams of the nitrogen cycle:

1) **Industrial processes** like the Haber Process produce ammonia and nitrate fertilisers directly from atmospheric nitrogen.

2) **Lightning** naturally converts nitrogen into nitrates.

Practice Questions

Q1 What process in living things extracts carbon dioxide from the air?

Q2 What is 'saprobiontic nutrition'?

Q3 What types of plants have root nodules?

Q4 In the nitrogen cycle, what chemical changes occur during 'nitrification'?

Exam Question

Q1 Explain how the carbon cycle has maintained the level of carbon dioxide in the atmosphere and how human activity has disrupted this balance.

[10 marks]

The Carbon and Nitrogen Cycles — surely, not again...

Here we are in A2 Biology and the Carbon and Nitrogen cycles are back again. When you realise that without nitrogen recycling bacteria, plants and animals couldn't exist, then you can see how important the cycles are. Perhaps that's why they keep cropping up, or perhaps the examiners are just torturing you — either way it's got to be learnt.

Investigating Numbers and Distribution

If you've been on an ecology field trip you'll be familiar with this stuff. You'll be relieved to know that you can revise this in the comfort of your own bedroom — you won't be asked to stand in a river catching horrible squirmy things.

You need to know how to take **Abiotic Measurements**

Temperature is easy enough — just use a **thermometer**.

pH measurements are only taken for soil or water. **Indicator** paper / liquid or an electronic **pH monitor** are used to get the data.

Light intensity is difficult to measure because it varies a lot over short periods of time. You get the most accurate results if you connect a **light sensor** to a data logger and take readings over a period of time.

Oxygen level only needs to be measured in aquatic habitats. An **oxygen electrode** is used to take readings.

Air humidity is measured with a hygrometer.

Moisture content of soil is calculated by finding the mass of a soil sample and putting it in an oven to dry out. The amount of mass that has been lost is worked out as a % of the original mass.

Quadrat Frames are a Basic Tool for Ecological Sampling

The method for using quadrats is described on page 27. Remember that samples must be taken **randomly**. It's also important to consider the **size** of the quadrat — smaller quadrats give more accurate results, but it takes longer to collect the data and they're not appropriate for large plants and trees.

Plotting a graph of cumulative number of species found against number of quadrats sampled should show you how many quadrats you'd need to sample in further studies of the same type of habitat.

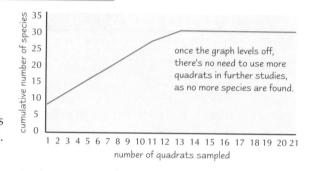

once the graph levels off, there's no need to use more quadrats in further studies, as no more species are found.

Point Quadrats are an alternative to quadrat frames

Pins are dropped through holes in the frame and every plant that each pin hits is recorded. If a pin hits several **overlapping** plants, **all** of them are recorded. A tape measure is laid along the area you want to study and the quadrat is placed at regular intervals (e.g. every 2 metres) at a right angle to the tape.

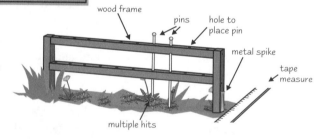

Line and **Belt Transects** are used to **Survey** an area

The line you select to sample across the area is called a **transect**. Transects are useful when you want to look for **trends** in an area e.g. the **distribution of species** from low tide to the top of a rocky shore.

A **line transect** is when you place a tape measure along the transect and record what species are touching the tape measure.

A **belt transect** is when data is collected between two transects a short distance apart. This is done by placing frame quadrats next to each other along the transect.

If it would take ages to count all the species along the transect, you can take measurements at set intervals, e.g. 1 m apart. This is called an **interrupted transect**.

The data collected from belt or line transects is plotted on a **kite diagram** (that's just a fancy kind of graph) and trends across the area can be observed.

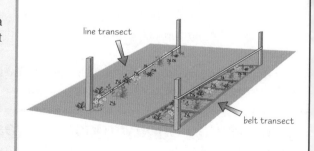

Investigating Numbers and Distribution

To sample Animals, you've got to Catch them

Most animals are **mobile** so they can't be sampled using quadrats or transects. There's various methods for catching animals depending on their **size** and the **kind of habitat** being investigated.

Nets can be used to trap flying insects and aquatic animals.

Pitfall traps are used to catch small walking organisms on land. They fall into the trap and are... well, trapped.

Pooters are used to catch individual insects which are chosen by the user.

Tullgren funnels are used to extract small animals from soil samples. The animals move away from the light and heat produced by the bulb and eventually fall through the barrier into the alcohol below the funnel.

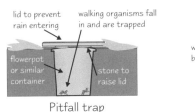

Pitfall trap

Tullgren funnel

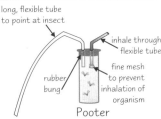

Pooter

The Mark-Release-Recapture Technique is for estimating Population Sizes

The mark-release-recapture method is basically this:

1) **Capture** a sample of the population.
2) **Mark** them in a harmless way.
3) **Release** them back into their habitat.
4) Take a **second sample** from the population.
5) **Count** how many of the second sample are marked.
6) Estimate the **size** of the whole population using the **Lincoln index**.

$$\text{Population size (S)} = \frac{n_1 \times n_2}{n_m}$$

n_1 = number of individuals in first sample
n_2 = number of individuals in second sample
n_m = number of marked individuals in the second sample

The accuracy of this method depends upon these **assumptions**:

1) The marked sample has had enough **time** and **opportunity** to **mix** back with the population.
2) The marking has not affected the individuals' **chances of survival**.
3) **Changes** in population size due to **births**, **deaths** and **migration** are **small**.
4) The marking has **remained visible** in all cases — so it needs to be waterproof.

Good ways of marking animals include using a UV pen or cutting a little bit of the animal's fur off.

Practice Questions

Q1 How would you calculate the moisture content of soil?

Q2 What is the difference between a line transect and a belt transect?

Q3 What piece of apparatus is used to extract small organisms from a soil sample?

Exam Questions

Q1 When measuring light intensity in an ecosystem, why is it not sufficient to take a single light-meter reading? [3 marks]

Q2 Under what circumstances would you use a transect rather than random sampling of an ecosystem? Give an example in your answer. [2 marks]

Q3 A population of woodlice were sampled using pitfall traps. 80 individuals were caught. The sample was marked and released. Three days later, a second sample was taken and 100 individuals were captured. Of these, 10 had marks. Use the Lincoln index to estimate the size of the woodlouse population. [2 marks]

What do you collect in a poo-ter again?

Aren't you glad that we don't use the mark-release-recapture technique to measure our population size. I don't fancy falling in a pitfall trap and then getting a chunk of my hair cut off. Seems kind of barbaric, now I think about it. When we did this experiment at school, we never caught any of the woodlice we'd marked again. They'd all disappeared...

Diversity

Diversity is all about how many different species there are in an ecosystem. In total, about 1.5 million species have been described but scientists reckon that the total number of species on Earth may be as high as 10 million.

There is a **Link** between **Diversity** and **Stability** in an ecosystem

Ecosystems with a **large diversity** of species tend to be **more stable** than those that are less diverse. There are two ways to tell how **stable** an ecosystem is:

> 1   Stable ecosystems are **resistant** to **change**.
>
> 2   If **disrupted** in some way, stable ecosystems return to their **original state** quite quickly.

If you think about it it makes sense — **low diversity** means that **predator** species don't have much **choice** of prey. If the population of a prey species is **reduced** or **wiped out**, then the predator species will be **at risk**.

When diversity is **higher**, the **predator** species will have a **large selection** of possible prey species. If one of the prey species is wiped out, there will still be plenty of other species that predators can eat.

1)   **Extreme** environments like **tundra**, **deserts**, **salt marshes** and **estuaries** are all ecosystems with **low diversities**. **Monocultures** are agricultural areas where only one crop is grown (e.g. wheat fields) — they have **artificially** low diversities. In areas of low diversity, plant and animal populations are mainly affected by **abiotic** factors.

2)   **Ecosystems** with **high diversities** are usually mature (i.e. old), and natural (e.g. oak woodlands), with environmental conditions that aren't too hostile. In these ecosystems populations are mostly affected by **biotic** factors.

Diversity is measured using a *'Diversity Index'*

The simplest way to measure diversity is just to count up the number of species. But that takes no account of the **population size** of each species. Species that are in an ecosystem in very **small** numbers shouldn't be treated the same as those with **bigger** populations.

A **diversity index** is an equation for diversity that takes different population sizes into account. You can calculate the diversity index (**d**) of an ecosystem like this:

Pete wasn't sure that the company's new increased diversity policy would be good for productivity.

$$d = \frac{N(N-1)}{\sum n(n-1)}$$

Where...

N = **Total number** of organisms of **all** species

n = **Total number** of **one** species

$\sum$ = '**Sum of**' (i.e. added together)

The **higher** the number the **more diverse** the area is. If all the individuals are of the same species (i.e. no diversity) the diversity index is 1.

Here's a simple example of the diversity index of a field:

There are 3 different species of flower in this field, a red species, a white and a blue.
There are 11 organisms altogether, so N = 11.
There are 3 of the red species, 5 of the white and 3 of the blue.
So the species diversity index of this field is:

$$d = \frac{11(11-1)}{3(3-1) + 5(5-1) + 3(3-1)} = \frac{110}{6 + 20 + 6} = 3.44$$

When calculating the bottom half of the equation you need to work out the n(n-1) bit for each different species then add them all together.

A variety of *Microclimates* leads to *Higher Diversity*

Microclimates are **small areas** where the **abiotic** factors are **different** from the surrounding area. For example, the underneath of a rock has a different microclimate than the top surface — it's cooler and more humid.

Each microclimate provides a slightly different **habitat** that will suit **certain species**. So, ecosystems that have a variety of microclimates can support a **high diversity**. Basically: **more microclimates = more species = higher diversity**.

Diversity

You need to know how to Use Quadrats

Ecologists look at three key **factors** when they're working out diversities:

SPECIES FREQUENCY	This is how **abundant** a species is in an area.
SPECIES RICHNESS	This is the **total number** of **different species** in an area.
PERCENTAGE COVER	This is how much of the surface is covered by a particular plant species (you can't use it for **animals** because they move around too much).

1) To measure all of these you use a piece of equipment called a **frame quadrat** — a square frame made from metal or wood. The area inside this square is known as a **quadrat**.

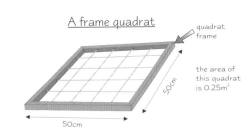

A frame quadrat

quadrat frame

the area of this quadrat is 0.25m²

50cm

50cm

2) **Quadrat frames** are **laid on the ground** (or the river / sea / pond bed if it's an aquatic environment). The **total number** of **species** in the quadrat frame is recorded as well as the number of **individuals** of each species.

3) Generally it's not practical to collect data for a whole area (it would take you ages) so **samples** are taken instead. This involves measuring lots of quadrats from different parts of the area. The data from the samples is then used to **calculate** the figures for the **entire area** being studied. **Random sampling** (see p.10) is used to make sure that there isn't any **bias** in the data.

4) **Species frequency** is measured by counting **how many quadrats** each species appears in and is given as a percentage (e.g. if a species was found in 5 out of 20 quadrat samples, the frequency would be 25%).

5) **Species richness** is measured by counting up the **total number of species** found in all the samples. You assume that the number of different species in your sample is the same as the number in the whole area that you are studying.

6) **Percentage cover** is measured by dividing the area inside the quadrat frame into a **10 × 10 grid** and counting **how many squares** each species takes up. Sometimes plants **overlap** so the total percentage cover ends up being **more** than **100%**.

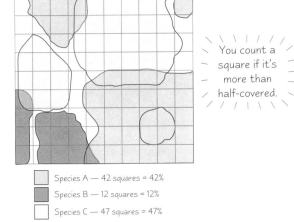

Measuring % cover

You count a square if it's more than half-covered.

Species A — 42 squares = 42%
Species B — 12 squares = 12%
Species C — 47 squares = 47%

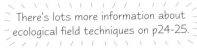

There's lots more information about ecological field techniques on p24-25.

Practice Questions

Q1 What is meant by a 'stable' ecosystem?

Q2 Give three examples of ecosystems that are likely to be unstable.

Q3 What is the difference between the diversity index and species richness?

Q4 Why do percentage cover measurements sometimes add up to more than 100%?

Exam Questions

Q1 Explain the link between the stability of an ecosystem and the diversity of species within it. [5 marks]

Q2 Describe in detail how you would measure the percentage cover of clover on a school field. [8 marks]

It's just all a bit random...

Well actually, that's the point, it's supposed to be random, or it wouldn't be a fair test. If you've used a quadrat, you've probably already realised it's just a fancy name for four bits of wood nailed together. They're probably expensive to buy, too. If you're a business studies student, you might see a money-making opportunity here, but get lost, because I saw it first.

Succession

Succession is all about how ecosystems change over time. Apart from a few fancy words I think that it's one of the easiest things in A2 biology — it's a lot more straightforward than the Krebs cycle and photosynthesis.

There are **Two** different types of **Succession**

Succession is sometimes called ecological succession in exams.

Succession is the process where **plant communities** gradually develop on **bare land**.
Eventually a **stable climax community** develops and after that big changes don't tend to happen.
There are **two** different types of succession...

Primary succession

Happens on land where there is no proper soil and **no living organisms**. New land created by a **volcanic eruption** is a good example of a place where primary succession will occur.

Secondary succession

Happens when most of the living organisms in an area are **destroyed**, but the **soil** and **some** living organisms remain. Examples include: woodland that has been burned by a **forest fire**, areas subject to severe **pollution**, or land that is cleared by **people** for things like **housing** or **new roads**.

Each stage in the succession of an area is called a **seral stage**. In every seral stage the plants change the environmental conditions, making them suitable for the next plants to move in.

You need to **Learn** an **Example** of succession

This example shows the seral stages that change **bare** sand dunes into **mature woodland**.

You need to learn this example, including all the names of the species.

The first plants to colonise an area have to be <u>specialised</u> so they can deal with the <u>harsh abiotic conditions</u>. These plants are known as <u>pioneer species</u>. They are usually herbaceous (non-woody).

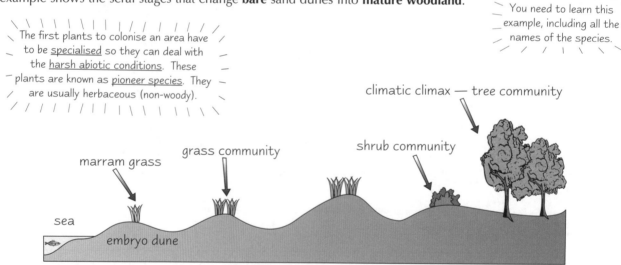

climatic climax — tree community

shrub community

grass community

marram grass

sea

embryo dune

1) The first **'pioneer'** species to colonise the area need to be able to cope with the **harsh abiotic conditions** on the **sand dunes** — there is **little fresh water** available, there are **high salt levels**, the **winds** are **strong** and there is **no proper soil**. Marram grass has good **xerophytic** adaptations (see page 45) so it is usually the first to start growing.

2) As the pioneer species begin to **die** they are broken down by microorganisms. The dead marram grass adds **organic material** to the sand creating a very basic 'soil' which can hold more water than plain sand.

3) This soil means that the abiotic conditions are **less hostile** and so other, less specialised grasses begin to grow.

4) These new grasses will eventually **out-compete** the original colonisers via **interspecific** competition.

5) As each new species moves in, more **niches** are created making the area suitable for even more species.

6) After the grass communities have all been out-competed, the area will be colonised by **shrubs** like **brambles**.

7) Eventually the area becomes dominated by **trees** — in Europe the trees will usually be things like **birch** and **oak**. The trees dominate because they prevent light from reaching the herbaceous plants below the leaf canopy.

Succession

Diversity Increases and Species Change as succession progresses

When succession happens in any environment the general pattern of change is always the same:

- The species present become **more complex** e.g. a forest starts with simple mosses and finishes with trees.
- The **total number** of organisms **increases**.
- The **number of species increases**.
- **Larger species** of plants arrive.
- **Animals** begin to move into the area — with each seral stage **larger** animals move in.
- **Food webs** become more **complex**.
- Overall, these changes mean that the ecosystem becomes more **stable**.

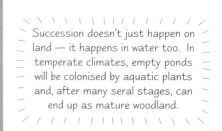
Succession doesn't just happen on land — it happens in water too. In temperate climates, empty ponds will be colonised by aquatic plants and, after many seral stages, can end up as mature woodland.

There are different Types of Climax Community

Various factors can **stop succession** going any further and lead to a **climax** community.
The climax is **classified** according to **what** has prevented the succession from going any further...

1) In a **climatic climax**, the succession has gone as far as the **climate** in the area will allow.
    E.g. Trees can't grow at high altitudes, so high up on alpine mountains the largest plants are **shrubs**.

2) **Human activities** can stop succession by felling trees, ploughing fields or grazing animals on farmland.
    Some ecosystems are deliberately 'managed' to keep them in a particular state, for example, the heather on moorland is burned every 5-7 years to prevent woodland from developing. When succession is stopped **artificially** like this the climax community is called a **plagioclimax**.

Farmland is an example of a Plagioclimax

Succession is stopped by regular **ploughing** or by the **grazing** of stock. In a grazed field, **grass** can survive because it is fast-growing, but slow growing plants get eaten before they can get established.

If the **grazing stops**, then slower growing plants can gradually begin to establish themselves. As they do, the **grass** will become **less dominant**. The new plant species will attract a wider range of **animals** and so the area will **increase** its **diversity**. Eventually, the field will become replaced by **woodland**.

Practice Questions

Q1   What is secondary succession?
Q2   What are the stages in succession called?
Q3   What is a pioneer species?
Q4   What name is given to a climax community brought about by human intervention?

Exam Questions

Q1   Define the term 'ecological succession', explaining how it occurs and
     the different types of climax communities that can be produced.   [8 marks]

Q2   a) Suggest three features of a plant species that might make it a successful pioneer species.   [3 marks]
     b) Suggest two reasons why such a pioneer species may disappear during the early stages of succession. [2 marks]

There are many different types of climax...

If your enthusiasm for all these Biology facts is waning, why not try reading some ICT... "Remote management supports users on a network. In the event of a significant problem or recurring error, the network administrator takes temporary control. Afterwards, the user can be advised on how to avoid similar problems in the future..." You see what I'm saying?

Deforestation

Forests are important for loads of reasons — they provide habitats for wildlife, they help balance atmospheric carbon and oxygen levels and they provide resources like wood and medicines. Excessive deforestation can lead to some problems...

There Isn't much Woodland Left

Britain used to be 85% covered in forest, now only about 8% is forest.
Deforestation has taken place for a number of reasons:

1) Trees have been removed for **timber**.
2) Trees have been used to make products like **paper** and **chipboard**.
3) Woodland has been cleared to make more room for **agriculture**.
4) Woodland has been cleared to allow for the building of **roads and houses**.

Deforestation Changes Abiotic Conditions

1) In a forest, most of the mineral nutrients are stored as **living biomass** in the trees. In autumn the trees drop their leaves and the minerals are **returned** to the **soil** where they are used again by plants growing in the spring. If the trees are removed from the habitat, the **minerals** are **lost** and the cycle is **interrupted**.

2) Removing trees makes the land more exposed to **wind** erosion. Tree roots usually bind the soil together, so when they are removed the soil structure becomes less stable.

3) Woodlands absorb a lot of **rainfall** — removing them creates greater risk of flooding and soil loss.

4) Once the trees are gone, the normal **plant succession** and animal community can't re-establish itself.

5) With fewer trees, there's **less transpiration** (see page 45) and less moisture in the air, so there's **less rainfall**.

6) The result of all this is a **plagioclimax** (see page 29) that isn't much good for growing anything.

Large scale deforestation has large scale effects because it affects the global balances of carbon dioxide (which is used in photosynthesis) and oxygen (which is given out by trees).

Forests are Important and Deforestation causes Problems

1) Forests use up **carbon dioxide** and produce **oxygen**. Every living organism needs oxygen. Without the forests, excess carbon dioxide in the air could contribute to global warming and worldwide climate change.

2) It's important to preserve **biodiversity** — i.e. to prevent species from becoming extinct. Once gone, extinct species can't be replaced.

3) A lot of **medicines** are based on chemicals from plants, trees and animals, many of them from forests, especially rainforests. A cure for a currently fatal disease could potentially be found in the rainforest — no one'll find it if the forest is destroyed.

4) Clearing and burning trees can affect urban areas. In 1998, **burning** of forests got **out of control** in Malaysia, which **polluted** the air for millions of people in densely populated Kuala Lumpur and Singapore.

Deforestation

Woodland can be Sustained by Good Management

Today, most woodland in the UK is used for either timber production or leisure.
Woodland is managed so that it can continue to provide habitats for wildlife.

Timber Production

Wood that is grown for timber is **deliberately** planted — species such as **pine** are used because they **grow quickly**. As soon as one crop of trees has been felled, more are planted.

Coppicing is a **traditional** method of timber production. Trees like hazel and sweet chestnut are cut down to their base so that they begin to sprout — each shoot is harvested when it matures. Coppicing produces lots of long poles without the trees themselves having to be felled.

Pollarding is similar — trees have their tops cut off to encourage the formation of a crown of branches.

a tree that has been coppiced

Leisure

Management for leisure use involves the creation of **mixed woodland** with paths and open spaces. Planting native shrubs like blackthorn, hawthorn and holly in shady parts of the wood can provide excellent habitats for birds such as wrens.

Dead wood is left where it is as it provides food and shelter for **fungi** and **invertebrates** like woodlice and wood-boring beetles. These are the foundation of many **food chains**, attracting many birds e.g. woodpeckers and nuthatches, bats and other small mammals. The management techniques needed to maintain mixed woodland are shown in the diagram...

Practice Questions

Q1 State three ways in which deforestation can damage the environment.

Q2 Why does deforestation increase soil erosion?

Q3 Why is woodland important in the global carbon budget?

Q4 What effect might deforestation have on health care?

Q5 Explain how deforestation could effect the climate.

Q6 Explain the difference between coppicing and pollarding.

Q7 Why is dead wood left on forest floors by foresters?

Exam Question

Q1 Describe ways in which woodland can be managed for sustained timber production. [4 marks]

If you go down to the woods today you might find that they've gone...

Excessive deforestation could have some major knock-on effects like species becoming extinct, increased atmospheric CO_2 levels, decreasing soil quality and changes in global climate. As you've probably noticed, deforestation has been on the political agenda for a while now so hopefully things will begin to change for the better soon.

Energy Supply and the Role of ATP

All animals and plants need energy for life processes and also for reading books like this.
This stuff is pretty tricky and we're diving in at the deep end, so hang on...

Biological processes need **Energy**

Cells need **chemical energy** for biological processes to occur. Without this energy,
these processes would stop and the animal or plant would just **die**... not good.

Energy is needed for **biological processes** like:
- active transport
- muscle contraction
- glycolysis (see p 34-35)
- reproduction and growth

Plants need energy for **metabolic reactions**, like:
- photosynthesis
- taking in minerals through their roots

ATP carries **Energy** around

It only **gets worse** from here on in for the rest of the section. But **don't worry**, ATP didn't make any sense to me at
first — it just clicked after many **painful hours** of reading dull books and listening to my teacher going on and on.
Here goes...

1)   ATP (**adenosine triphosphate**) is a **small water-soluble** molecule that is easily transported around cells.

2)   It's made from the nucleotide base **adenine**, combined with a **ribose sugar** and **three phosphate groups**.

3)   ATP is a **phosphorylated nucleotide** — this means it's a nucleotide with extra phosphate groups added.

4)   ATP **carries energy** from **energy-releasing** reactions to **energy-consuming** reactions.

How ATP carries energy:

1) ATP is **synthesised** from **adenosine diphosphate (ADP)** and an **inorganic phosphate** group using the energy produced by the **breakdown of glucose**. The enzyme **ATPsynthase** catalyses this reaction.

2) ATP **moves** to the part of the cell that requires energy.

3) It is then **broken down** to ADP and **inorganic phosphate** and **releases chemical energy** for the process to use. **ATPase** catalyses this reaction.

4) The ADP and phosphate are **recycled** and the process starts again.

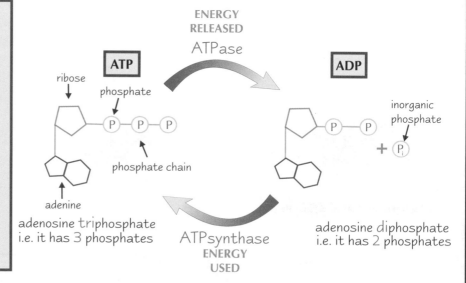

Cells Release Energy (to make **ATP**) by **Respiration**

Cellular respiration is the process where cells **break down glucose**, it produces carbon dioxide and water and
releases **energy**. The energy is used to **produce ATP** from ADP and P_i. There are two types of respiration:

1) **Aerobic respiration** — respiration **using oxygen**.

2) **Anaerobic respiration** — respiration **without oxygen** (see page 38 for more). Both types produce ATP.

You need to learn the summary equation for **aerobic respiration**.

$$C_6H_{12}O_6 \text{ (glucose)} \ + \ 6O_2 \implies 6CO_2 \ + \ 6H_2O \ + \textbf{Energy}$$

Energy Supply and the Role of ATP

Respiration takes place in the Mitochondria of the Cell

1) **Mitochondria** are present in all **eukaryotic** (i.e. plant, animal, fungi and protoctist) cells. They're 1.5 to 10 µm long.

2) Cells that use lots of energy, e.g. **muscle cells**, **liver cells** and the middle section of **sperm**, have lots of mitochondria.

3) The **inner membrane** of each mitochondrion is folded into **cristae** — structures that increase surface area.

4) **ATP** is produced via the **stalked particles** on the cristae of the inner mitochondrial membrane, in a stage called the **electron transport chain** (see page 37).

5) The **Krebs Cycle** (page 36) takes place in the **matrix** of mitochondria.

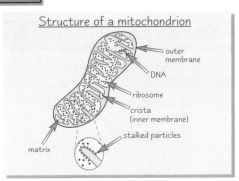

Structure of a mitochondrion

Respiration is a Metabolic Pathway

There are some pretty confusing technical terms about reactions in this section. If you do chemistry you'll be laughing — if not, you'd better concentrate:

- **Metabolic pathway** — a **series** of **small reactions**, e.g. respiration or photosynthesis, controlled by enzymes.

- **Catabolic reactions** — breaking **large molecules** into **smaller ones** using enzymes, e.g. breaking down glucose in respiration.

- **Anabolic reactions** — combining **smaller molecules** to make **bigger ones** using enzymes.

- **Phosphorylation** — adding **phosphate** to a molecule, e.g. ADP is phosphorylated to ATP.

- **Hydrolysis** — the **splitting** of a molecule using **water**.

- **Photolysis** — the **splitting** of a molecule using **light** energy.

Redox reactions — reactions that involve **oxidation** and **reduction**.

1) If something is **reduced** it has **gained electrons**, and lost oxygen or gained **hydrogen**.
   If something is **oxidised** it has **lost electrons**, and gained oxygen or lost **hydrogen**.

2) Oxidation of one thing always involves reduction of something else.

3) The enzymes that catalyse redox reactions are called **oxidoreductases**.

4) Respiration and photosynthesis are riddled with redox reactions.

Oxidation	Reduction
electrons are lost	electrons are gained
oxygen is added	oxygen is lost
hydrogen ions are lost	hydrogen ions are gained

One way to remember electron movement is "OILRIG" = Oxidation Is Loss of e⁻, Reduction Is Gain of e⁻.

Practice Questions

Q1 How is energy released from ATP?

Q2 Write down five metabolic processes in animals which require energy.

Q3 What is the purpose of the cristae in mitochondria?

Q4 What's the difference between anabolic and catabolic reactions?

Q5 What does hydrolysis mean?

Exam Questions

Q1 What is the connection between phosphate and the energy needs of a cell? [2 marks]

Q2 ATP is a small, water-soluble molecule which can be rapidly and easily converted back into ADP if ATPsynthase is present. Explain how these features make ATP suitable for its function. [3 marks]

I've run out of energy after that little lot...

You really need to understand what ATP is, because once you start getting bogged down in the complicated details of respiration and photosynthesis, at least you'll understand why they're important and what they're producing. It does get more complicated on the next few pages, so take your time to understand the basics before you turn the page.

Glycolysis and the Link Reaction

You can split the process of respiration into four parts — that way you don't have to swallow too many facts at once. The first bit, glycolysis, is pretty straightforward.

Glycolysis is the First Stage of Respiration

So, to recap... most cells use carbohydrates, usually glucose, for respiration.

> Glycolysis splits **one molecule** of glucose into **two** smaller molecules of **pyruvate**.

Glucose is a hexose (6-carbon) molecule.
Pyruvate is a triose (3-carbon) molecule.
Pyruvate is also known as pyruvic acid.

1) Glycolysis is the first stage of respiration (see the map to the right).
2) It takes place in the **cytoplasm** of cells.
3) It's the **first stage** of both aerobic and anaerobic respiration, and **doesn't need oxygen** to take place — so it's **anaerobic**.

Respiration Map

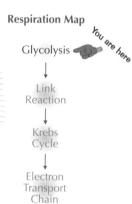

Glycolysis *You are here*
↓
Link Reaction
↓
Krebs Cycle
↓
Electron Transport Chain

There are Two Stages of Glycolysis — Phosphorylation and Oxidation

✦ 1 ✦ Stage One — Phosphorylation

1) Glucose is **phosphorylated** by adding 2 **phosphates** from 2 molecules of ATP.
2) Glucose is split using water (**hydrolysis**).
3) 2 molecules of **triose phosphate** and 2 molecules of ADP are created.

✦ 2 ✦ Stage Two — Oxidation

1) The triose phosphate is **oxidised** (loses hydrogen), forming **two** molecules of **pyruvate**.
2) **Coenzyme NAD$^+$** collects the hydrogen ions, forming **2 reduced NAD (NADH + H$^+$)**.
3) **4 ATP** are produced, but 2 were used up at the beginning, so there's a **net gain of 2 ATP**.

A coenzyme is a helper molecule that carries chemical groups or ions about, e.g. NAD removes H$^+$ and carries it to other molecules.

A 1
B 2

These arrows in diagrams just mean that A goes into the main reaction and is converted to B. A will normally release or collect something from molecule 1, e.g. hydrogen or phosphate.

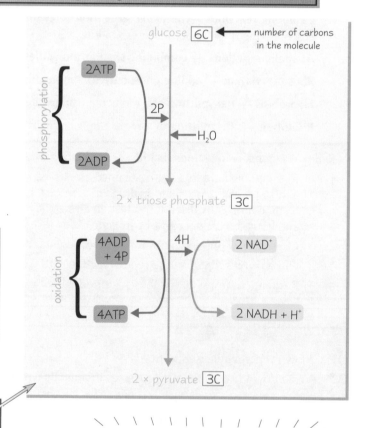

glucose [6C] ← number of carbons in the molecule

phosphorylation
2ATP
2P
H$_2$O
2ADP

2 × triose phosphate [3C]

oxidation
4ADP + 4P
4H
2 NAD$^+$
4ATP
2 NADH + H$^+$

2 × pyruvate [3C]

A triose phosphate is just a simple 3-carbon sugar with a phosphate group attached. Different books use different names, but this is the easiest to remember.

Next in Aerobic Respiration...

1) The **2** molecules of **reduced NAD** go to the **electron transport chain** (see page 37).
2) The **two pyruvate** molecules go in to the matrix of the **mitochondria** for the **link reaction** (a small reaction that **links** glycolysis to the second stage, the **Krebs cycle**). It's so exciting I bet you can't wait...

Glycolysis and the Link Reaction

The **Link Reaction** converts **Pyruvate** to **Acetyl Coenzyme A**

The link reaction is fairly simple and goes like this:

1) One **carbon atom** is removed from pyruvate in the form of CO_2.

2) The remaining **2-carbon molecule** combines with **coenzyme A** to produce **acetyl coenzyme A** (**acetyl CoA**).

3) Another oxidation reaction occurs when **NAD⁺** collects more **hydrogen ions**. This forms **reduced NAD** (**NADH + H⁺**).

4) **No ATP** is produced in this reaction.

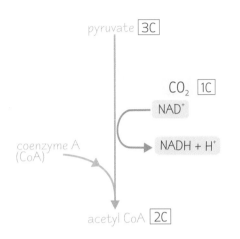

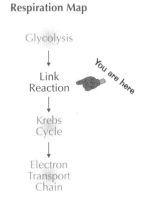

Respiration Map

Glycolysis
↓
Link Reaction   You are here
↓
Krebs Cycle
↓
Electron Transport Chain

The **Link Reaction** occurs **Twice** for every **Glucose Molecule**

1) For each **glucose molecule** used in glycolysis, **two pyruvate** molecules are made.

2) But the **link reaction** uses only **one pyruvate** molecule, so the **link reaction** and the **Krebs cycle** happen **twice** for every glucose molecule which goes through glycolysis.

The **Products** of the **Link Reaction** go to the **Krebs Cycle** and the **ETC**

So for each glucose molecule:

- Two molecules of **acetyl coenzyme A** go into the Krebs cycle (see next page).
- Two **carbon dioxide molecules** are released as a waste product of respiration.
- Two molecules of **reduced NAD** are formed and go into the **electron transport chain** (which is covered on the next two pages).

Practice Questions

Q1 What do the terms hydrolysis and phosphorylation mean?

Q2 Why is there only a net gain of 2 ATP during glycolysis?

Q3 Where is acetyl CoA formed?

Q4 Name all the products of the link reaction.

Exam Questions

Q1 Describe simply how a 6-carbon molecule of glucose can be changed to pyruvate. [5 marks]

Q2 Describe what happens in the link reaction. [4 marks]

Acetyl Co-what?

It's all a bit confusing, but you need to know it, so it's worth taking a bit of time to break it down into really simple chunks. Don't worry too much if you can't remember all the little details straight away. If you can remember how it starts and what the products are, you're getting there. You'll get the hang of it all eventually, even if it seems hard right now.

Krebs Cycle and the ETC

And now we have the third and fourth stages of the respiration pathway. Keep it up — you're nearly there.

The **Krebs Cycle** is the **Third Stage** of *Aerobic Respiration*

The Krebs cycle takes place in the **matrix** of the mitochondria. It happens once for each pyruvate molecule made in glycolysis, and it goes round twice for every glucose molecule that enters the respiration pathway.

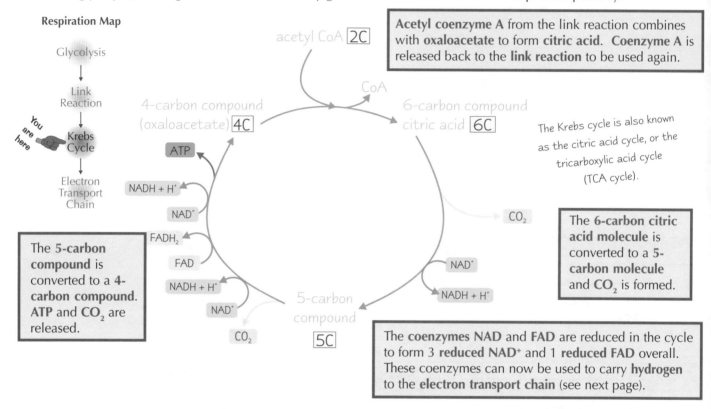

Respiration Map

Glycolysis

Link
Reaction

You are here → Krebs Cycle

Electron
Transport
Chain

acetyl CoA 2C

Acetyl coenzyme A from the link reaction combines with **oxaloacetate** to form **citric acid**. Coenzyme A is released back to the **link reaction** to be used again.

CoA

4-carbon compound
(oxaloacetate) 4C

6-carbon compound
citric acid 6C

ATP

The Krebs cycle is also known as the citric acid cycle, or the tricarboxylic acid cycle (TCA cycle).

NADH + H⁺

NAD⁺

CO_2

FADH₂

FAD

NADH + H⁺

NAD⁺

The 5-carbon compound is converted to a 4-carbon compound. ATP and CO_2 are released.

NAD⁺

NADH + H⁺

The **6-carbon citric acid molecule** is converted to a 5-carbon molecule and CO_2 is formed.

5-carbon compound 5C

CO_2

The **coenzymes NAD and FAD** are reduced in the cycle to form 3 **reduced NAD⁺** and 1 **reduced FAD** overall. These coenzymes can now be used to carry **hydrogen** to the **electron transport chain** (see next page).

Products of the **Krebs Cycle** are used in the *Electron Transport Chain*

Some products are **reused**, some are **released** and others are used for the **next stage** of respiration:

- One **coA** is **reused** in the next **link reaction**.
- **Oxaloacetate** is **regenerated** so it can be **reused** in the next **Krebs cycle**.

- Two **carbon dioxide** molecules are released as a **waste product** of respiration.
- One molecule of **ATP** is made per turn of the cycle — by **substrate level phosphorylation.**

- **Three reduced NAD** and **one reduced FAD** co-enzymes are made and carried forward to the **electron transport chain**.

The **Electron Transport Chain** is the **Final Stage** of *Aerobic Respiration*

Before we get too bogged down in all the details, here's what the electron transport chain is all about:

All the products from the previous stages are used in this final stage. Its purpose is to **transfer** the **energy** from molecules made in glycolysis, the link reaction and the Krebs cycle to ADP. This forms **ATP**, which can then deliver the energy to parts of the cell that need it.

The electron transport chain is where **most of the ATP** from respiration is produced. In the whole process of aerobic respiration, **32 ATP molecules** are produced from one molecule of glucose: 2 ATP in glycolysis, 2 ATP in the Krebs cycle and 28 ATP in the electron transport chain.

The electron transport chain also **reoxidises NAD and FAD** so they can be reused in the previous steps.

Krebs Cycle and the ETC

The **Electron Transport Chain** produces **lots of ATP**

The **electron transport chain** uses the molecules of **reduced NAD** and **reduced FAD** from the previous three stages to produce **28 molecules of ATP** for every molecule of glucose.

1) **Hydrogen atoms** are released from **NADH + H$^+$** and **FADH$_2$** (as they are oxidised to NAD$^+$ and FAD). The H atoms **split** to produce **protons (H$^+$)**, and **electrons (e$^-$)** for the chain.

2) The **electrons** move along the electron chain (made up of three **electron carriers**), losing energy at each level. This energy is used to **pump** the **protons (H$^+$)** into the space **between** the inner and outer **mitochondrial membranes** (the **intermembrane space**).

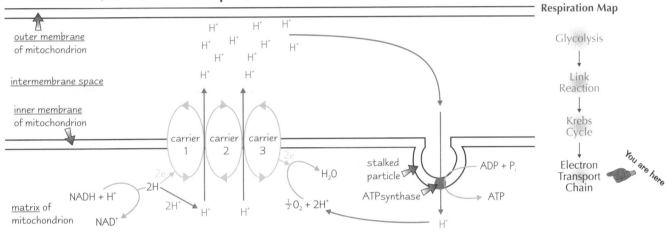

3) The **concentration** of protons is higher in the intermembrane space than in the mitochrondrial matrix, so an **electrochemical gradient** exists.

4) The **protons** then move back through the inner membrane **down** the **electrochemical gradient**, through specific channels on the **stalked particles** of the **cristae** — this drives the enzyme **ATPsynthase.** By 'spinning like a motor', this enzyme supplies **electrical potential energy** to make **ATP** from ADP and inorganic phosphate.

5) The **protons** and **electrons** recombine to form **hydrogen**, and this combines with **molecular oxygen** (from the blood) at the end of the transport chain to form **water**. Oxygen is said to be the final **electron acceptor**.

The **synthesis of ATP** as a result of the energy released by the electron transport chain is called **oxidative phosphorylation**.

This is how the **electron transport chain** produces **28** molecules of **ATP** from **1** molecule of **glucose**:

- **1** turn of the Krebs cycle produces **4** molecules of **reduced NAD** (including 1 from the **link reaction**) and **1** of **reduced FAD**.
- **2** molecules of **pyruvate** enter the Krebs cycle for **each** molecule of **glucose**, so overall **8 NAD$^+$** and **2 FAD** are reduced.
- **2 reduced NAD** are also produced from the first part of respiration, **glycolysis** (see p. 36).
- Each **reduced NAD** can produce **2.5 ATP**, and each **reduced FAD** can produce **1.5 ATP**.
- So: 8 reduced NAD + 2 reduced NAD = 10 reduced NAD. **10 × 2.5 = 25 ATP.** **2 reduced FAD × 1.5 = 3 ATP.** In total, 25 + 3 = **28 molecules of ATP**.

(There are also **2 ATP** produced by **glycolysis**, and **2** for each molecule of glucose in the **Krebs cycle** = **32 ATP** produced in total by **respiration**.)

Practice Questions

Q1 How many molecules of CO_2 are made in one turn of the Krebs cycle?

Q2 Name the two coenzymes that are reduced in the Krebs cycle.

Q3 Which molecule finally accepts the electrons passed down through the electron transport chain?

Exam Question

Q1 Calculate the number of ATP molecules that are produced by aerobic respiration from one molecule of glucose. Show your working in detail.
[14 marks]

Cheers for that Mr Krebs...

...you can keep your cycle, in future. Phew, this biochemistry stuff is tough going. The key to learning this stuff is to learn the big facts first — glycolysis, link reaction, Krebs cycle, electron transport chain. Once you know what the main parts are and roughly what happens at each stage, you stand some chance of learning the more detailed stuff.

The Biochemistry of Respiration

There's two ways to release energy — aerobic respiration and anaerobic respiration. Simple.

Aerobic respiration provides more Energy

There are a few important differences between aerobic and anaerobic respiration:

Anaerobic Respiration	Aerobic Respiration
Does not need oxygen	Needs oxygen
Takes place in cytoplasm	Takes place in cytoplasm and mitochondria
Uses glycolysis and alcoholic or lactate fermentation	Uses glycolysis, Krebs cycle, link reaction and the electron transport chain
Pyruvate not completely oxidised	Pyruvate oxidised in link reaction
Can follow either of two metabolic pathways 1. alcoholic fermentation 2. lactate fermentation	Follows one metabolic pathway
Produces 2 ATP for every glucose	Produces 32 ATP for every glucose

In **aerobic** respiration, about **32 ATP** molecules are made for every glucose molecule (see page 37).

In **anaerobic** respiration, only **2 ATP** molecules are made (during glycolysis).

So **aerobic** respiration releases **loads more energy** than **anaerobic** respiration.

There are Two forms of Anaerobic Respiration

The **two different kinds** of anaerobic respiration are:

1) **Lactate fermentation** — used by **animals**.

2) **Alcoholic fermentation** — used by **plants** and **microorganisms** like yeast.

They both occur in the **cytoplasm**, and both start with the **glycolysis reaction**.

Lactate Fermentation Occurs in Animal Cells

Some animal cells can respire without oxygen for a short time when they need to:

1) It starts with glycolysis, producing pyruvate (see page 34).

2) **Pyruvate is reduced to lactic acid** (lactate) by adding **two H atoms** from **reduced NAD**.

3) **NAD** is returned to glycolysis to be **used again**. Pretty simple, really.

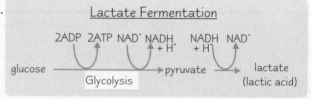

Alcoholic Fermentation makes Alcohol

Some industrial processes like brewing and breadmaking use fermentation reactions to help produce their products. The most useful products that **microorganisms** produce by fermentation are **alcohol** and **carbon dioxide**.

1) Alcoholic fermentation starts with **glucose (6C)**. The process of glycolysis turns this into **pyruvate (3C)** (see p 34).

2) CO_2 is removed from pyruvate to form **ethanal (2C)**.

3) The **reduced NAD** made in glycolysis is **reoxidised** and transfers **two hydrogen atoms** to ethanal to form **ethanol**.

4) The **reoxidised NAD** can then be reused in **glycolysis**.

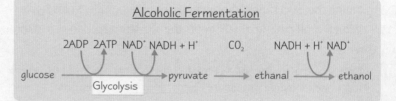

Fermentation reactions are normally carried out on an industrial scale in vessels called **fermenters** or **bioreactors**.

The Biochemistry of Respiration

The Respiratory Quotient (RQ) tells you what Substrate is being Respired

During aerobic respiration, oxygen is consumed and carbon dioxide is produced.

RQ (Respiratory Quotient) is the amount of **carbon dioxide** produced, **divided** by the amount of **oxygen consumed** in a set period of time. It's useful because it shows what **kind** of substrate is being used for **oxidation**, and what sort of **metabolism** an organism has.

$$RQ = \frac{\text{Molecules of } CO_2 \text{ produced}}{\text{Molecules of } O_2 \text{ used}}$$

This is the basic equation for aerobic respiration using glucose:

$$C_6H_{12}O_6 + 6O_2 \longrightarrow 6CO_2 + 6H_2O + \text{Energy}$$

RQ = molecules of CO_2 produced ÷ molecules of O_2 used

= 6 ÷ 6 = 1.

So if cells only used pure glucose, the RQ would always just be 1. But **most cells don't just use glucose**...

Different Substrates have Different RQ Values

Under normal conditions, the **usual RQ** for humans is between **0.7** and **1.0**. An RQ in this range shows that some **fats** (lipids) are being used for respiration as well as carbohydrates like glucose. Protein isn't normally used for respiration by the body unless there's nothing else.

Respiratory Substrate	RQ
Lipids (triglycerides)	0.7
Proteins or amino acids	0.9
Carbohydrates (e.g. glucose)	1
Anaerobic respiration of carbohydrate	> 1

1) **High RQs** (greater than 1) often mean that an organism is short of oxygen, and having to respire **anaerobically** as well as aerobically.

2) If the organism is respiring **lipids** the RQ will be **lower than 1**. This is because more oxygen is needed to oxidise fat than to oxidise carbohydrate.

3) **Plants** sometimes have a **low RQ**. This may be because the CO_2 released in respiration is used for **photosynthesis** (so it's not measured).

Practice Questions

Q1 Why is anaerobic respiration so inefficient compared to aerobic respiration?
Q2 Which type of anaerobic respiration occurs in animals?
Q3 What is the final product of alcoholic fermentation?
Q4 Give the expression used to calculate RQ.
Q5 Write out the equation for the aerobic respiration of glucose.
Q6 When is protein used as a respiratory substrate?

Exam Questions

Q1 a) Compare and contrast the two forms of anaerobic respiration. [10 marks]
b) In terms of the amount of ATP produced, how much more efficient is aerobic respiration at releasing energy than anaerobic respiration? [3 marks]

Q2 The equation for the respiration of the fat tripalmitin is $2C_{51}H_{98}O_6 + 145O_2 \longrightarrow 102CO_2 + 98H_2O$. What is the RQ for tripalmitin? [2 marks]

Did somebody mention beer...

The basics of respiration aren't that bad. It's not overly-complicated, and fermentation even has some rather tasty products. That makes it a lot more interesting than most of this section, I reckon. This is the stuff that makes biology slightly less tedious, so you've got no excuse for not learning this.

The Biochemistry of Photosynthesis

Don't worry if this seems hard at first. Read it through carefully a couple of times, and it'll start to make sense.

The **Equation** for **Photosynthesis** isn't too bad

Here's the overall equation for photosynthesis. Hopefully it'll look pretty familiar. When you were doing your GCSEs this little equation was all you had to worry about, but those days are long gone, my friend.

$$6CO_2 + 6H_2O + \text{Energy} \xrightarrow{\text{chlorophyll}} C_6H_{12}O_6 + 6O_2$$

Chloroplasts are the Site of *Photosynthetic Reactions*

1) Chloroplasts are usually about **5 μm** in diameter.

2) They're surrounded by a double membrane called the **chloroplast envelope**.

3) **Thylakoids** (fluid-filled sacs) are stacked up inside the chloroplast into structures called **grana**. These structures have a large surface area. The thylakoids are where the **light-dependent reaction** of photosynthesis occurs.

4) **Chlorophyll** and other photosynthetic pigments are found on the **thylakoid membranes**. They form a complex called **photosystem II** (see page 41). Some thylakoids have **extensions** that join them to thylakoids in other grana. These are called **inter-granal lamellae**, and they're the sites of **photosystem I** (see page 41).

5) The thylakoids are embedded in a gel-like substance called the **stroma**. The stroma is where the **light-independent reaction** of photosynthesis (called the **Calvin cycle**) happens. It contains **enzymes** (for the Calvin cycle), **sugars** and **organic acids**.

6) Carbohydrates produced by photosynthesis and not used straight away are stored as **starch grains** in the **stroma**.

Diagram labels: inner membrane of envelope, outer membrane, thylakoids, thylakoid membrane, stroma, lamella, stalked particles, starch grain, one granum (stack of thylakoids)

Photosynthesis can be Split into *Two Stages*

Photosynthesis happens in the **chloroplasts**, and nowadays you need to know that it consists of two **stages**:

1) The **light-dependent reaction** (which, as the name suggests, needs **light energy**) takes place in the **thylakoid membranes** of the chloroplasts. Light energy is absorbed by pigments in the **photosystems** (see below), and used to provide the energy for the next stage — the light-independent reaction. There are **two different reactions** going on in this next stage — **cyclic photophosphorylation** and **non-cyclic photophosphorylation**. The plant can **switch between** the two, depending on whether it needs **reduced NADP** or just **ATP** (see below).

2) The **light-independent reaction** or **Calvin cycle** (which, as the name suggests, doesn't use light energy) happens in the **stroma** of the chloroplast. The **ATP** and the **reduced NADP** molecules that were made in the light-dependent reaction supply the **energy** to make **glucose**. See pages 42-43 for more on the Calvin cycle.

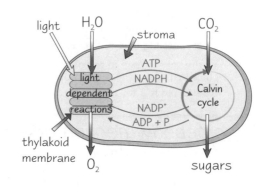

The diagram shows how the two different reactions, light-dependent and light-independent, fit together in the chloroplast.

The Biochemistry of Photosynthesis

Photosystems I and II capture Light Energy

1) **Photosystems** are made up of **chlorophyll a**, **accessory pigments** (like **chlorophyll b** and **carotenoids**) and **proteins**. The proteins hold the pigment molecules in the best positions for **absorbing** light energy and **transferring** this energy to the **reaction centre** of the photosystem.

2) The **reaction centre** is a particular **chlorophyll molecule** called a **primary pigment**. The energy from absorbing light is passed from one **accessory pigment** to another until it reaches this **primary pigment**.

3) The energy is then used to **excite** pairs of **electrons** in the reaction centre pigment. The electrons move up to a higher **energy level**, ready to be used in the **light dependent reactions**.

4) There are **two** different photosystems used by plants to capture light energy. **Photosystem I** (or PSI) uses a chlorophyll molecule that absorbs light at wavelength **700 nm** in its reaction centre. PSI is found mostly in the **lamellae** in a chloroplast. **Photosystem II** (PSII) uses a chlorophyll molecule that absorbs light best at around **680 nm** in its reaction centre. It's found mostly in the **thylakoids** of the chloroplast.

The Light-Dependent Reaction makes ATP in Photophosphorylation

The **energy** captured by the photosystems is used for **two** main things:

1) Making **ATP** from **ADP** and **inorganic phosphate** (**phosphorylation**). It's called **photo**phosphorylation here, as it uses **light**.

2) Splitting **water** into **H⁺** ions and **OH⁻** ions. This is called **photolysis**, because the splitting (lysis) is caused by light energy (photo). Photolysis is covered on the next page.

Photophosphorylation involves the **excited electrons** in the reaction centre of a photosystem being passed to a special molecule called an **electron acceptor**. These electrons are then passed along a **chain** of other electron carriers, each at a slightly **lower energy level** than the one before, so that the electrons **lose energy** at every stage in the chain. The energy given out is used to add a phosphate molecule to a molecule of ADP — and this is photophosphorylation.

You don't need to know the actual mechanism in detail, but it's very similar to how ATP is produced in **respiration**, involving the flow of **hydrogen ions** (H⁺) through **stalked particles** (which you can read all about on page 37). The H⁺ ions used in photosynthesis come from the **photolysis of water**, which is covered on the next page.

The difference between **cyclic** and **non-cyclic photophosphorylation** is in what happens to those electrons that have been moving through the chain of carriers. This is also explained on the next page.

Cyclic Photophosphorylation just produces ATP

Cyclic photophosphorylation only uses **photosystem I**. It's called cyclic photophosphorylation because the electrons from the chlorophyll molecule are simply **passed back** to it after they've been through the chain of carriers — i.e. they're **recycled** and can be used repeatedly by the same molecule. This **doesn't** produce any **reduced NADP** (**NADPH + H⁺**), but there **is** enough energy to make **ATP**. This can then be used in the **light-independent reaction**.

Practice Questions

Q1   What is the full equation for photosynthesis?

Q2   Where in the chloroplast does the light-independent reaction of photosynthesis happen?

Q3   What is the reaction centre of a photosystem?

Q4   What two main things is the light energy captured by photosystems used for?

Exam Question

Q1   a) Precisely where in the plant does the light-dependent stage occur? [1 mark]
     b) Which two compounds produced in the light-dependent stage are used in the light-independent stage? [2 marks]
     c) Which of the light-dependent reactions of photosynthesis are involved in producing these compounds? [3 marks]

Photophosphorylate that, if you can...

If you're feeling filled with despair as you read this tip, well, don't. You **will** understand this, don't give up. I guarantee it'll seem clearer every time you go through it, until at last you're left wondering what all the fuss was about. By the way, don't be put off when it says protons instead of hydrogen ions. That always confused me, but they mean the same thing.

The Biochemistry of Photosynthesis

Here's the rest of the stuff on photosynthesis... It ain't pretty, but it's here and it's all yours. Have fun and learn it well.

Non-cyclic Photophosphorylation produces ATP, NADPH and Oxygen

Non-cyclic photophosphorylation uses both **PSI** and **PSII**. It involves **photolysis**, which is the splitting of **water** using light energy. Photolysis only happens in **PSII**, because only PSII has the right **enzymes**.

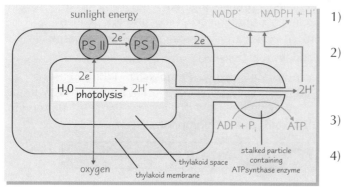

1) Light energy enters **PSII** and is used to move electrons to a **higher energy level**.

2) The electrons are passed along the chain of electron carriers to **photosystem I**. Most of the energy lost by the electrons during this process is used to make **ATP** (like in cyclic photophosphorylation).

3) Light energy is absorbed by PSI, which excites the electrons **again** to an **even higher energy level**.

4) The electrons are passed to a **different electron acceptor**, and **don't** return to the chlorophyll.

5) For the chlorophyll to keep working, the electrons have to be replaced from **somewhere else** — so they're taken from a molecule of **water** (water is the electron donor). This makes the water molecule split up into **protons** (H^+) and **oxygen**.

6) The **protons** (H^+) from the water molecule combine with the **electrons** currently with the second electron acceptor to give **hydrogen atoms**. These are used to react with a substance called **NADP** to produce **NADPH** and H^+. These are needed for the **light-independent reaction** (see below).

So when electrons move back from the **second electron acceptor** to the chlorophyll molecule, that's **cyclic** photophosphorylation. If they don't, and the replacement electrons come from **water** instead, that's **non-cyclic**.

	cyclic photophosphorylation	non-cyclic photophosphorylation
photosystem	I	I and II
what's needed	light, ADP, phosphate	light, water, NADP, ADP, phosphate
what's produced	ATP	ATP, NADPH + H^+, O_2

The Light-Independent Reaction is also called the Calvin Cycle

The Calvin cycle makes **hexose sugars** (sugars with **6 carbons**, like **glucose** and **fructose**) from **carbon dioxide** and a **5-carbon** compound called **ribulose bisphosphate**. It happens in the **stroma** of the chloroplasts. There are a few steps in the reaction, and it needs **energy** and H^+ ions to keep the cycle going. These are provided by the products of the **light-dependent reaction**, ATP and **reduced NADP** (NADPH + H^+).

The diagram shows what happens at each stage in the cycle. The numbers in brackets (5C, 3C etc.) show how many **carbon atoms** there are in each molecule — the cleverest bit of the cycle is how it turns a **5-carbon** compound into a **6-carbon** one.

1) CO_2 enters the leaf through the **stomata** and diffuses into the **stroma** of the chloroplast.

2) There it's taken up by **ribulose bisphosphate (RuBP)**, a **5-carbon** compound. This gives an **unstable 6-carbon** compound, which quickly breaks down into **two** molecules of a **3-carbon** compound called **glycerate 3-phosphate (GP)**.

3) This reaction is catalysed by the enzyme **ribulose bisphosphate carboxylase (rubisco)**.

4) **ATP** from the **light-dependent stage** of photosynthesis is now used to provide the energy to turn the **3-carbon** compound, **GP**, into a **different** 3-carbon compound called **triose phosphate**.

5) This reaction also needs H^+ ions, which are provided by the **reduced NADP** (NADPH + H^+) made in the **light-dependent reaction**.

6) **Two** triose phosphate molecules then **join together** to give **one hexose sugar** (e.g. glucose).

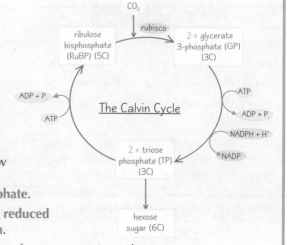

The Biochemistry of Photosynthesis

Five out of every **six** molecules of **triose phosphate** produced in the Calvin cycle are **not** used to make hexose sugars, but to **regenerate** RuBP. Making RuBP from triose phosphate molecules uses the rest of the ATP produced by the light-dependent reaction.

The Calvin cycle is the starting point for making **all** the substances a plant needs — plants can't take in **proteins** and **lipids** like animals can.

- Other **carbohydrates**, like **starch**, **sucrose** and **cellulose**, can be easily made by joining the simple hexose sugars together in different ways.
- **Lipids** are made using **glycerol** synthesised from **triose phosphate**, and **fatty acids** from **glycerate 3-phosphate**.
- **Proteins** are made up of **amino acids**, which are also synthesised from **glycerate 3-phosphate**.

The **Calvin Cycle** needs to turn **6 times** to make **1 Glucose Molecule**

Five out of every **six triose phosphate molecules** go back into the cycle to regenerate **RuBP**, rather than going to make new hexose sugars. This means that the cycle has to happen **six times** just to make one new sugar. The box below shows why.

*Remember, the photosynthesis equation uses **6 CO₂**.*

1) **6 RuBP** and **6 CO₂** molecules (i.e. 6 turns of the cycle) convert a total of **12 glycerate 3-phosphate** molecules into **12 triose phosphate molecules**.

2) **Two** molecules of **triose phosphate** are removed from the cycle and make **one glucose molecule**.

3) **10 triose phosphate** molecules regenerate the RuBP.

This might seem a bit inefficient, but it keeps the cycle going and makes sure that there's always **enough RuBP** there ready to combine with CO₂ taken in from the atmosphere.

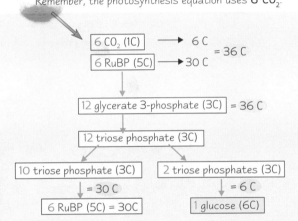

Practice Questions

Q1 Give two examples of a hexose sugar.

Q2 How many carbon atoms are there in a molecule of triose phosphate?

Q3 Name the enzyme that catalyses the reaction between carbon dioxide and ribulose bisphosphate.

Q4 How is the Calvin cycle involved in making lipids?

Q5 How many CO₂ molecules need to enter the Calvin cycle to make one glucose?

Exam Questions

Q1 Which molecule in photosynthesis:
   a) is the carbon dioxide acceptor? [1 mark]
   b) provides the hydrogen ions to reduce glycerate 3-phosphate? [1 mark]
   c) is regenerated in the Calvin cycle? [1 mark]
   d) is known as rubisco? [1 mark]
   e) is made of 5 carbon atoms? [1 mark]

Q2 Look at the diagram on the right and describe what is happening:
   a) between points a and b, [1 mark]
   b) between points b and c, [1 mark]
   c) at point c. [1 mark]

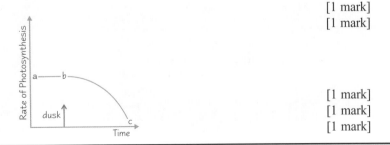

Don't let the light-independent stage destroy you as it did Obi-Wan...

Now don't start sinking into despair again. I know it's a lot to take coming after that last page, but actually this one is probably a bit easier. Learn that cycle on the last page and you're three quarters of the way there. Don't worry too much about learning the maths bit in the box on this page either — as long as you've got the general gist, that's enough.

Water Uptake in Plants

Brace yourself for a couple of jam-packed pages.

Water Enters a Plant through its Root Hair Cells

Water has to get from the **soil**, across the **root** and into the **xylem**, which takes it up the plant. The bit of the root that absorbs water is covered in **root hairs**. This increases its surface area and speeds up water uptake. Once it's absorbed, the water has to get through two root tissues, the **cortex** and the **endodermis**, to reach the xylem.

> Water always moves from areas of higher water potential to areas of lower water potential — it goes down a water potential gradient. The soil around roots has a high water potential (i.e. there's lots of water there) and leaves have a low water potential (because water constantly evaporates from them). This creates a water potential gradient that keeps water moving through the plant in the right direction, from roots to leaves. Plants also actively transport ions such as nitrates into their root hair cells — this lowers the water potential so even more water moves in by osmosis.

There are Two Routes Water can take through the Root

Water can travel through the roots into the xylem by two different paths:

1) The **apoplast pathway** — goes through the **non-living** parts of the root — the **cell walls**. The walls are very absorbent and water can simply diffuse through them, as well as passing through the spaces between them.

2) The **symplast pathway** — goes through the **living** cytoplasm of the cells. The **cytoplasm** of neighbouring cells connects through **plasmodesmata** (they're little strands that pass through small gaps in the cell walls).

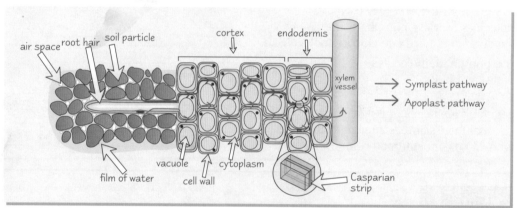

Both pathways are used, but the main one is the **apoplast pathway** because it provides the **least resistance**. When the water gets to the **endodermis** cells, though, the apoplast pathway is blocked by a **waxy strip** in the cell walls, called the **Casparian strip**, which the water can't penetrate. Now the water has to take another pathway. This is useful, because it means the water has to go through a **cell membrane**. Cell membranes are able to control whether or not substances in the water get through. Once past the endodermis, the water moves into the **xylem**.

Xylem Transports Water and Provides Support

There are **three** ways that water moves up through the xylem **against** the **force of gravity**:

1) The **cohesion-tension theory** explains how water moves up plants from roots to leaves, against the force of gravity.
   - Water evaporates from the leaves at the 'top' of the xylem (through transpiration).
   - This creates a tension, which pulls more water into the leaf.
   - Water molecules **stick together** ('cohesion'), due to hydrogen bonds, so when some are pulled into the leaf others follow.
   - This means the whole **column** of water in the xylem, from the leaves down to the roots, moves upwards by mass flow.

2) **Root pressure** also helps move the water upwards. The endodermis pushes ions into the xylem by active transport so a water potential gradient develops. This pushes water into the xylem which shoves the water that's already in the xylem further up. This pressure is weak, and couldn't move water to the top of bigger plants by itself. It helps though, especially in young, small plants where the leaves are still developing.

3) **Capillarity** is when water moves up a thin tube. In plants it happens because of the molecular attraction (adhesion) between water and the inside of the xylem tube.

Scientists reckon that water movement actually takes place through a **combination** of these **three** methods — none of them is **powerful** enough to move it on their own.

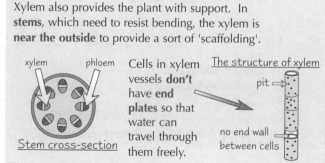

Xylem also provides the plant with support. In **stems**, which need to resist bending, the xylem is **near the outside** to provide a sort of 'scaffolding'.

Cells in xylem vessels **don't** have **end plates** so that water can travel through them freely.

Stem cross-section

The structure of xylem

pit

no end wall between cells

Water Uptake in Plants

Transpiration is Loss of Water from a Plant's Surface

Transpiration happens because there has to be **holes** (stomata) in the leaves to let gases (**carbon dioxide** and **oxygen**) exchange during photosynthesis and respiration. Water **evaporates** from the moist cell walls and accumulates in the spaces between cells in the leaf. Then it diffuses out of the **stomata** when they open. This happens because there is a **diffusion gradient** — there's more water inside the leaf than in the air outside.

A <u>potometer</u> is a special piece of apparatus used to <u>measure transpiration</u>. It actually measures <u>water uptake</u> by a plant, but it's assumed that uptake by the roots is <u>directly related</u> to water loss by the leaves. This lets you see how different factors affect the transpiration rate.

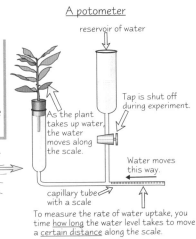

A potometer

reservoir of water

As the plant takes up water, the water moves along the scale.

Tap is shut off during experiment.

Water moves this way.

capillary tube with a scale

To measure the rate of water uptake, you time <u>how long</u> the water level takes to move a <u>certain distance</u> along the scale.

Four Main Factors Affect Transpiration Rate

The factors below affect transpiration rate. Temperature, humidity and wind alter the **diffusion gradient**, but **light** is a bit different:

1) **Light** — Transpiration happens mainly when the stomata are open. In the dark the stomata usually close, so there's little transpiration.

2) **Temperature** — Diffusion involves the movement of molecules. Increasing the temperature speeds this movement up. So as temperature rises, so does transpiration rate.

3) **Humidity** — If the air around the plant is humid, the **diffusion gradient** between the leaf and the air is reduced. This slows transpiration down.

4) **Wind** — Lots of air movement blows away water molecules from around the stomata. This **increases** the diffusion gradient, which increases the rate of transpiration.

Xerophytic Plants are adapted to Dry Conditions

In **deserts** (where water is **scarce**) and in **arctic** regions (where it's **frozen**), plants need special adaptations to avoid dehydration. Natural selection has meant that plants which are successful in arid environments are **efficient** at **water uptake** and have facilities to **reduce transpiration** and **store water**. Plants that are specially adapted to live in dry conditions are called **xerophytes**.

Cacti are adapted to desert conditions:

1) **Transpiration** is reduced by various leaf adaptations — a **thick waxy cuticle**, few stomata, sunken stomata, stomata that **open at night** and **close by day**, and a leaf surface covered with **fine hairs**.

2) **Water uptake** is **increased** by having an **extensive root system** which covers a wide area.

3) Water is **stored** in **fleshy, succulent** leaves or stems. Cacti also have **spines** to **protect** the plant from predators.

Practice Questions

Q1   What is the difference between the apoplast and symplast pathways?

Q2   What are the two roles of xylem in plants?

Q3   Explain the cohesion-tension theory of water movement in plants.

Q4   Explain how you use a potometer.

Exam Question

Q1   Explain why movement of water in the xylem stops if the leaves of a plant are removed.   [4 marks]

Don't worry if it takes you a long time to learn these pages

There's absolutely masses to learn here, and lots of it isn't easy. So I'm afraid you'll need to spend a bit of time on these pages before you'll know it all well enough for the exam. Try learning it in small chunks and test yourself as you go along. Don't forget to look at the diagrams too — they contain lots of information that you need to know.

Homeostasis and Temperature Control

This page is all about keeping things constant inside the body.
Everything has to be carefully balanced — otherwise your body would be totally out of control.

Homeostasis keeps the Internal Environment Constant

Homeostasis keeps the **blood** and the **tissue fluid** that surrounds the cells
(the **internal environment**) within **certain limits**, so the cells can function normally.
Changes in the external environment can affect the internal one, which can **damage cells**:

1) **Temperature** changes affect the rates of metabolic reactions, and high temperatures can denature proteins.

2) **Solute concentrations** affect **water potentials** of solutions
and therefore the loss or gain of water by cells due to osmosis.

3) Changes in **pH** can affect the function of proteins by changing their shapes.

Homeostasis keeps the internal environment **constant**, avoiding **cell damage**.

A Homeostatic System detects a Change and Responds to it

1) A **receptor detects** a change (the **stimulus**).

2) The receptor communicates with the part of the body that brings
about a response (the effector), via the **nervous system** or **hormones**.

3) An **effector** brings about the response. Glands and muscles are effectors.

Negative feedback keeps the internal environment **constant**:

Changes in the environment trigger a response that
counteracts the changes — e.g. a **rise** in temperature
causes a response that **lowers body temperature**.

This means that the **internal environment** tends to stay
around a **norm**, the level at which the cells work best.

This only works within **certain limits** —
if the environment changes too much, then
the effector may not be able to **counteract** it.

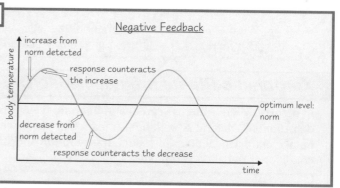

Mammals often use several **different responses** to keep a system in homeostasis. This lets them control things better,
e.g. temperature control (see next page) and control of blood glucose concentration (see pages 47-49).

Animals are Ectotherms or Endotherms

All organisms release **heat energy** from their metabolism, which increases body temperature. Body heat can be
exchanged with other solid objects by **conduction** or **radiation** and lost to air by **convection** or by **evaporation**.
Animals are either **ectothermic** or **endothermic**. Endothermic animals have more control over their body temperature:

<table>
<tr><td>

Ectotherms

1) E.g. invertebrates, fish, amphibians and reptiles.

2) Their body temperature depends on the temperature
of the external environment.

3) They have a **variable** metabolic rate, and often
generate very little heat.

4) The temperature of their surroundings determines
their **activity levels**: they're more active and eat
more at higher temperatures.

5) They can regulate their temperature only by changing
their behaviour, e.g. many reptiles are **heliotherms**
— they gain heat by basking in the sun.

</td><td>

Endotherms

1) E.g. mammals and birds.

2) Their body temperature is largely **independent**
of external temperature (within certain limits).

3) They have a constantly **high** metabolic rate
so they generate a lot of heat.

4) They have efficient mechanisms for
thermoregulation (regulation of body
temperature), so are less affected by the
temperature of their surroundings.

</td></tr>
</table>

Homeostasis and Temperature Control

Mammals can Regulate their Body Temperature

The **skin** has a surface **epidermis**, and a thicker, deeper **dermis** with features for temperature control:

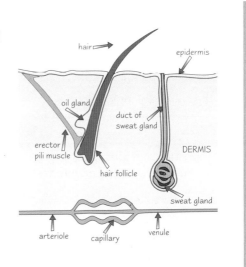

1) The skin has lots of **blood capillaries**. When you're too hot, the arterioles dilate (**vasodilation**), and more blood flows through the capillaries in the surface layers of the dermis to release more heat by **radiation**. When you're too cold, the arterioles constrict (**vasoconstriction**), reducing heat loss.

2) In mammals, **sweat** is secreted from **sweat glands** when the body is too hot. Sweat evaporates from the surface of the epidermis, using **body heat** and so cooling the skin.

3) Mammals have a layer of hair to provide **insulation** by trapping air, which is a poor heat-conductor. When it's cold, the **erector pili muscles** contract, which raises the hairs, trapping more air and preventing heat loss.

Thermoregulation is controlled by the Autonomic Nervous System

Body temperature is regulated by the unconscious actions of the **autonomic nervous system** (see pages 76-77):

1) If the external temperature **rises**, this stimulates thermoreceptors in the skin dermis, which send action potentials along **sensory neurones** to the hypothalamus. The **heat loss centre** in the **anterior hypothalamus** sends **action potentials** (see p. 68-69) along **motor neurones** to effectors in the skin. The effectors cause **vasodilation** of arterioles and more sweat secretion, so **more heat** is lost from the skin. The production of certain **hormones** is **decreased**, which decreases the metabolic rate so less heat is generated.

2) If the external temperature **falls**, the **heat gain centre** in the **posterior hypothalamus** causes dermal arterioles to constrict and erector pili muscles to contract, erecting the hairs and trapping more air. The hypothalamus stimulates the production of a hormone to **increase** the **metabolic rate**, generating heat from **increased respiration**.

Practice Questions

Q1   Define homeostasis.

Q2   Give two factors that are controlled by homeostasis in the body of a mammal.

Q3   For one of your chosen factors, explain why it is beneficial to control it.

Q4   What is the difference between the external environment and the internal environment?

Exam Questions

Q1   a) Explain what is meant by the term 'negative feedback'.   [2 marks]
     b) Give two examples of factors that are controlled by a negative feedback mechanism.   [2 marks]

Q2   The rate of food consumption of a lizard (reptile) and a mouse (mammal) were compared. It was found that overall the mouse consumed a greater percentage of its own body mass in food per day than the lizard. However, the rate of food consumption by the lizard increased as temperature increased from 20°C to 30°C. There was no significant change in rate of food consumption in the mouse as temperature increased. Explain the differences between the lizard and the mouse.   [6 marks]

My biology teacher often gave me negative feedback...

The key to understanding homeostasis is getting your head round negative feedback. It's not complicated — if one thing goes up, the body responds to bring it back down, or vice versa. Temperature control and blood glucose control (p48-49) are the two examples that you need to know for the exam.

Blood Glucose Control

Ever felt a 'sugar rush' after eating eighteen packets of Refreshers? OK, maybe no one else eats that many at once. These two pages are about how your body deals with all the glucose you get from your food.

Many Factors can change the Blood Glucose Concentration

Glucose enters the blood from the **small intestine** and dissolves in the blood plasma. Its concentration usually stays around **100mg per 100cm³ of blood**, but some factors can change this level:

1) Blood glucose concentration **increases** after consuming food, especially if it's **high** in carbohydrate.
2) Blood glucose concentration **falls** after exercise, because more glucose is used in respiration to release energy.

Big changes in the concentration of blood glucose can **damage cells** by changing the water potential.

The Pancreas secretes Hormones to control Blood Glucose Levels

Two hormones — **insulin** and **glucagon**, regulate blood glucose concentration. They're secreted by clusters of cells in the **pancreas** called the **Islets of Langerhans**. These cells detect changes in blood glucose concentration.

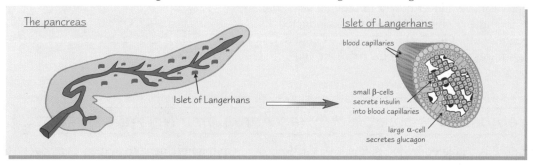

Controlling Blood Glucose Levels is an example of Negative Feedback

Insulin and glucagon work together to regulate the blood glucose concentration by **negative feedback** (pages 46-47):

When there's a rise in blood glucose concentration...

1) The glucose molecules bind to receptors in the cell membranes of small **beta (β) cells** in the Islets of Langerhans.
2) These cells secrete **insulin** into the blood.
3) Insulin molecules bind to receptors in the cell membranes of **hepatocytes** (liver cells) and other cells, e.g. muscle cells.
4) This **increases** the **permeability** of the hepatocyte cell membranes to glucose, so more glucose is absorbed.
5) Inside the hepatocytes, the insulin activates an **enzyme** that catalyses the condensation of glucose molecules into **glycogen**, which is stored in the cytoplasm of the hepatocytes, and in the muscles. This process is called **glycogenesis**.
6) Insulin also increases the rate of respiration of glucose in other cells. The blood glucose concentration **decreases**.

When there's a fall in blood glucose concentration...

1) The larger **alpha (α) cells** of the Islets of Langerhans secrete the hormone **glucagon** into the blood.
2) Glucagon binds to receptors on the **hepatocytes**.
3) This activates an **enzyme** inside the hepatocytes that catalyses the **hydrolysis** of stored glycogen into **glucose**. This process is called **glycogenolysis**.
4) The blood glucose concentration **increases**.

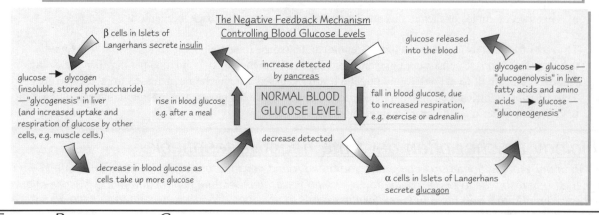

Blood Glucose Control

Diabetes causes problems with Glucose Regulation

Diabetes mellitus is a condition where blood glucose concentration can't be regulated properly. There are **two** main types of diabetes:

Type 1 Diabetes

In **Type 1** diabetes, the pancreas doesn't produce enough insulin. After eating, the blood glucose level rises and stays high (**hyperglycaemia**). The kidneys can't reabsorb this glucose, so it's **excreted** in the urine.
The symptoms include tiredness, thirst and weight loss. It can be treated by regular **injections** of insulin, and **controlling carbohydrate intake** from the diet. The amount of insulin injected has to be carefully controlled, because too much can produce a dangerous drop in blood glucose levels (**hypoglycaemia**).

Type 2 Diabetes

Type 2 diabetes is usually acquired later in life. This type of diabetes is linked with obesity. Blood insulin levels are normal or high, but the **receptor proteins** on the hepatocyte cell membranes don't work properly. The symptoms are the same as for Type 1 diabetes. It can usually be controlled by reducing **carbohydrate** intake.

Insulin used to treat diabetes is produced by **genetic engineering**.
Genetically engineered insulin is considered better than the old method of using insulin from pigs because:

- There's less chance of the body producing anti-insulin **antibodies** against the 'foreign' peptide.
- There's less risk of contracting a **virus** than from the animal insulin.
- The 'human' insulin works more **quickly** in humans than pig insulin.

Practice Questions

Q1   Give one factor that will increase blood glucose concentration, and one that will reduce it.
Q2   What are the roles of the alpha and beta cells of the Islets of Langerhans?
Q3   State two effects of insulin on liver cells.
Q4   Describe two ways in which diabetes mellitus can be controlled.
Q5   Why is it best to treat diabetes with insulin produced by genetic engineering?

Exam Questions

Q1 a) Explain the role of the endocrine system in returning the blood glucose level to normal
after consuming a meal that has a high glucose content.   [10 marks]

   b) Some sufferers of diabetes can produce insulin, but still cannot regulate
their blood glucose levels effectively. Suggest a reason for this.   [2 marks]

Q2   Explain why glucagon levels in the blood increase during exercise.   [5 marks]

My glucose levels are low — pass the chocolate...

Learn this carefully, or you'll end up getting your hormones confused. And make sure you're clear on the different types of diabetes too — people with Type 1 can't produce enough insulin, people with Type 2 produce it fine, but can't respond to it. Now eat a huge meal, wait for your blood glucose levels to rise, then draw that diagram from page 48 until you know it.

Methods of Removing Nitrogenous Waste

These next few pages deal with all the ways that the body gets rid of the things we don't need, like nitrogenous waste and Westlife albums.

Waste Products can be Toxic

All **metabolic processes** produce **waste products**, for example **digestion** produces **excess amino acids** (see below). These waste products are **toxic** if they build up within an organism and so there are usually mechanisms to control their levels.

In Mammals the Liver gets rid of Waste Products

The **liver** acts as a **homeostatic organ** (see pages 46-47) in three ways:
1)   It controls **blood sugar levels** by controlling glycogen and glucose levels (see pages 48-49).
2)   It controls **fats** in the body by processing fatty acids and controlling cholesterol and phospholipid levels.
3)   It gets rid of excess **amino acids** by **deamination** (see below).

Substances that contain **nitrogen** can't usually be stored by the body for use later on. Proteins contain **amino acids**, and nitrogen is part of the **amino group**, NH_2.

Animals often eat protein with **more amino acids** than the body can use at once. Some amino acids are used to make **useful proteins**, but the **excess** ones need to be **converted** to other things. This happens in the **liver**.

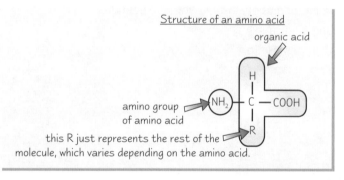

Structure of an amino acid

Excess Amino Acids have their Amino Groups Removed

The excess amino acids are carried in the blood stream from the small intestine to the liver where they are processed:

1)   Nitrogen-containing **amino groups** from the excess amino acids are removed, forming **ammonia** and **organic acids**. This is **deamination**. The organic acids are respired or converted to carbohydrate and stored as glycogen.

2)   Ammonia is too poisonous for mammals to excrete it directly, so the **ammonia** reacts with **carbon dioxide** to form safer **urea**.

3)   Urea is formed in the **ornithine cycle**. The ammonia is taken up by a molecule called ornithine and used to make the less toxic **urea**. One **urea** molecule is released for every turn of the cycle, and ATP gets used up too.

4)   The urea is released into the blood, then **excreted** from the body by the **kidneys**.

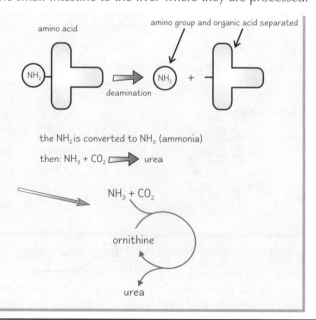

the NH_2 is converted to NH_3 (ammonia)

then: $NH_3 + CO_2 \Longrightarrow$ urea

$NH_3 + CO_2$

ornithine

urea

Methods of Removing Nitrogenous Waste

Freshwater Fish excrete Ammonia

1) Fish live in aquatic environments so they can excrete their nitrogenous waste directly into the water.

2) Freshwater fish excrete the simplest form of nitrogenous waste — **ammonia**, which is highly soluble.

3) To make ammonia the excess amino acids are **deaminated**, but they **aren't** converted to urea.

4) Because freshwater fish have a plentiful supply of **water** they can **dilute** the ammonia (which is highly **toxic** when **concentrated**) with lots of water before they excrete it in their urine.

5) Some of the ammonia also **diffuses** through the **gills** where **counter-current flow** maintains a high **concentration gradient** between the fluid in the gills and the water outside the fish.

6) Marine (sea-living) fish don't use this system — they need to **save** water to prevent dehydration. So they do the same as **mammals** and convert the ammonia to **urea**.

Insects, Birds and Reptiles need to Save Water

Animals that live in dry environments or need to conserve water can't excrete nitrogenous waste in **solution** (with lots of water).

Birds and insects excrete **uric acid** which isn't soluble in water — this allows them to reabsorb the water in their rectums rather than excreting it. The excretion produced by insects and birds is a **semi-solid** paste. Producing uric acid in this way means that birds and insects can save water and **prevent dehydration**.

Because uric acid isn't as toxic as urea it can be **stored** in the body for longer meaning that excretion can take place less frequently — this saves even more water.

Practice Questions

Q1 What are the three ways in which the liver acts as a homeostatic organ?
Q2 Outline the reactions involved in the formation of urea from excess amino acids.
Q3 Which organs of the body are responsible for excreting waste products?
Q4 What happens to amino acids that are *not* excess to the body's requirements?
Q5 In what form do birds excrete their excess nitrogenous waste?

Exam Questions

Q1 Explain why the urea concentration in the urine will rise after consumption of a meal that is rich in protein. [6 marks]

Q2 Explain why urea is not formed in the body of a freshwater fish. [4 marks]

Better out than in...

The best thing about this page is that explains why snake pee is solid. If you've ever kept snakes, you'll know I'm telling the truth. And now you know the science behind it... If only all of A2 Biology was made up of fascinating facts like that (sigh). Still, there's only a few things to learn on this page, and they're not so hard, really.

Kidney Function

You've learnt how urea is produced, so now complete the picture by learning exactly how the kidneys excrete all the stuff our bodies don't need any more. Then have some steak and kidney pie.

The **Kidneys** are **Organs** of **Excretion**

1) Urea produced by the liver is **excreted** from the body by the **kidneys**. Urea is dissolved in the blood plasma.

2) When the blood passes through the kidney nephrons (the tubes that run through the kidneys — see below for more on these), liquid is filtered out of the blood, carrying small solutes with it, including **urea**.

3) The useful solutes are reabsorbed, and the waste products are removed from the body in **urine**.

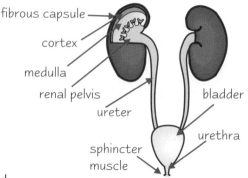

You need to know about **two main stages** of kidney function — **ultrafiltration** in the renal capsules (also called the Bowman's capsules) and **selective reabsorption** in the medulla.

Don't get mixed up — urea is one specific substance, but urine is a mixture that contains urea.

Ultrafiltration in the kidneys takes place in the **Renal Capsules**

Blood enters the kidney cortex through the **renal artery**, then goes through millions of knots of capillaries in the kidney cortex. Each knot, (**glomerulus**) is a bundle of capillaries looped inside a hollow ball called a **renal** (or Bowman's) **capsule**. An **afferent arteriole** takes blood into each glomerulus, and an **efferent arteriole** takes blood out.

Ultrafiltration takes place in all body tissues that have capillaries. Blood pressure squeezes liquid from the blood through the capillary wall. Small molecules and ions pass through, but larger ones like proteins and blood cells stay behind in the blood. In most parts of the body, this liquid gathers between the cells as tissue fluid. In the kidney, the liquid collects in microscopic **tubules**. Useful substances are **reabsorbed** back into the blood, and waste substances (like dissolved urea) are excreted in the urine.

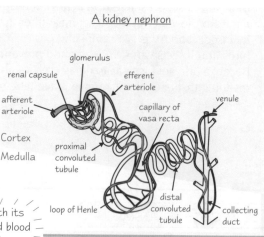

A kidney nephron

One tubule system with its associated capsule and blood supply is called a nephron.

Ultrafiltration in the capillary and renal capsule membranes

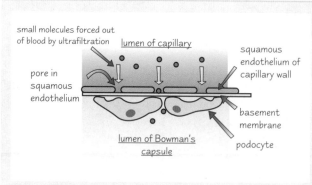

Small molecules and ions pass from blood in the glomerular capillary into the renal capsule through:

1) Pores in the **capillary wall** (the wall is made of one layer of flat cells — squamous endothelium).

2) A **basement membrane** made up of collagen fibres and glycoprotein.

3) A specialised epithelium of the renal capsule, made up of cells called **podocytes**. These support the membrane while letting the filtrate pass through.

Kidney Function

Useful substances are Reabsorbed

Filtrate from the renal capsule enters the **proximal convoluted tubule** in the cortex of the kidney. The wall of this tubule is made of **cuboidal epithelium**, with **microvilli** facing the filtrate to increase the surface area.

Blood leaving the glomerulus along the efferent arteriole enters another capillary network, called the **vasa recta**, that's wrapped around the proximal convoluted tubule. This provides a big surface area for **reabsorption** of useful materials from the **filtrate** (in the tubules) into the **blood** (in the capillaries) by:

1) **active transport** of glucose, amino acids, vitamins and some salts

2) **osmosis** of water

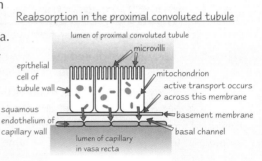
Reabsorption in the proximal convoluted tubule

Water is reabsorbed from the Whole Tubule

Water enters the blood by **osmosis** because the water potential of the blood is **lower** than that of the filtrate. Most of the water is reabsorbed from the **proximal convoluted tubule**. Reabsorption from the **distal convoluted tubule** and **collecting duct** is controlled by **hormones**.

Urine is a Mixture of substances dissolved in Water

Urine usually contains the following things:

1) **Variable amounts** of **water** and **dissolved salts**, depending upon how much you've drunk (see pages 54-55).

2) **Variable amounts** of **dissolved urea**, depending upon how much protein you've eaten (see pages 50-51).

3) Other substances such as hormones and water-soluble vitamins.

It **doesn't** usually contain:

1) **Proteins**, because they're too big to be filtered out in the renal capsule (they can't pass through the basement membrane).

2) **Glucose, amino acids or vitamins**, because they're actively reabsorbed back into the blood from the proximal convoluted tubule.

3) **Blood cells**.

Practice Questions

Q1 Describe the process of ultrafiltration.

Q2 Name three components of the filtrate of a nephron that will be reabsorbed back into the blood from the proximal convoluted tubule.

Q3 What are the names of the processes that account for the reabsorption of substances?

Exam Questions

Q1 a) Suggest how the features of the proximal convoluted tubule of a kidney nephron maximise the rate of absorption of glucose. [5 marks]

b) Suggest why a smaller quantity of urea passes from the tubule into the blood than glucose. [3 marks]

Q2 Occasionally some people produce urine that contains traces of protein. Suggest an explanation for this. [2 marks]

It's steak and excretion organ pie for dinner...

The kidneys are pretty complicated organs. That's why it's so serious when they go wrong — all that toxic urea would just stay in your blood and poison you. If your kidneys fail you'll end up hooked up to a machine for hours every week so it can filter your blood, unless some kind person donates a new kidney for you.

Water Balance

You should have a rough idea about how the kidneys work by now, so here's a bit more detail on how they help with homeostasis. Read. Learn. Enjoy.

The **Kidneys** regulate the body's **Water Content (Osmosregulation)**

Mammals excrete urea in solution, so **water** is lost too. The kidneys regulate the levels of water in the body.

1) If the body is **dehydrated** (e.g. if the body has lost a lot of water by sweating), then more water is **reabsorbed** by osmosis from the tubules of the nephron, so less water is lost in the urine.

2) If the body has a **high water content** (e.g. from drinking a lot), then **less** water is reabsorbed from the tubules, so more water is lost in the urine.

This regulation takes place in the middle and last parts of the nephron — the **loop of Henle**, the **distal convoluted tubule** and the **collecting duct**. The **volume** of water reabsorbed is controlled by hormones.

The **Loop of Henle** has a **Countercurrent Multiplier Mechanism**

This sounds really scary, but stick with it, it's not too complicated really:

Just between the proximal and distal convoluted tubules is a part of the nephron called the **loop of Henle**. It's made up of two 'limbs'.

1) Water leaves the **descending limb** of the loop by osmosis, and Na^+ and Cl^- ions diffuse into the loop. This makes the **ion concentration** of the tubule **higher** towards the **base** of the loop.

2) The Na^+ and Cl^- ions are then actively pumped out of the top of the **ascending limb** of the loop into the medulla. The high concentration of Na^+ and Cl^- ions in the medulla causes water to leave the collecting duct and descending limb by **osmosis**.

3) The water is then **reabsorbed** into the blood through the **capillary network**.

This mechanism is called the **countercurrent multiplier**.

The countercurrent multiplier mechanism lets land-living mammals produce urine with a **solute concentration** higher than that of the blood, so they can avoid losing too much water. The volume of water reabsorbed can be **regulated** depending on the needs of the body.

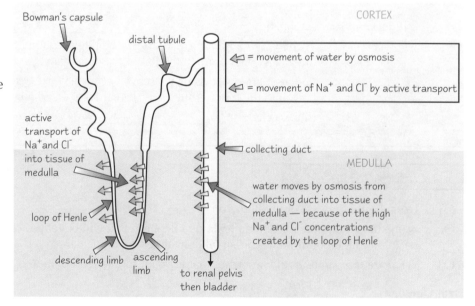

Another hard day studying reading, writing and the countercurrent multiplier mechanism.

Water Reabsorption is controlled by Hormones

A hormone released from the **posterior pituitary gland**, called **antidiuretic hormone (ADH)**, makes the walls of the distal convoluted tubules and collecting ducts **more permeable** to water. More water is then **reabsorbed** from these tubules into the medulla (and then into the blood) by **osmosis**. This means that **less water** is lost in the urine.

It's called antidiuretic hormone because diuresis is when lots of dilute urine is produced.

Water Balance

Blood ADH levels are High when you're Dehydrated

Dehydration is what happens when you **lose water**, e.g. by sweating during exercise:

1) The water content of the blood drops, so its water potential drops.
2) This is detected by osmoreceptors in the hypothalamus.
3) This stimulates the pituitary gland to release more ADH into the blood.
4) The ADH increases the permeability of the walls of the collecting ducts in the kidneys, so more water is reabsorbed back into the blood by osmosis.
5) Less water is lost in the urine.

Blood ADH levels are Low when your body is Hydrated

If you drink lots of water, more water is absorbed from the gut into the **blood**, and the **excess** is lost in the **urine**:

1) The water content of the blood rises, so its **water potential rises**.
2) This is detected by the **osmoreceptors** in the **hypothalamus**.
3) This stimulates the **pituitary gland** to release **less ADH** into the blood.
4) Less ADH means that the collecting ducts are less permeable, so **less water** is **reabsorbed** into the blood by **osmosis**.
5) **More water** is lost in the urine.

Kangaroo Rats are adapted to Dry Conditions

Kangaroo rats live in the **deserts** of north America. They are so well adapted to the dry conditions that they never drink... pretty amazing huh? The only water they ingest is a small amount of water from their food. Instead of drinking they use a combination of **physiological** and **behavioural** adaptations to **make** and **retain** water:

Other desert animals have features so that they can cope with the dry conditions. For example, some desert frogs have waterproof skin.

1) They use the water produced in respiration — metabolic water. And they metabolise **fat** because it produces **twice** as much water as **carbohydrate** does.
2) When they breathe through their **noses** the inhalation has a cooling effect on the nasal passages. The water vapour in the exhaled air **condenses** against the nasal passages, reducing water loss.
3) They don't **sweat**.
4) They spend most of their day in a deep **burrow**, feeding at **night** when the temperature is much **cooler**.
5) They produce **dry faeces** to save as much water as possible.
6) They have very long loops of Henle, so there's a greater **surface area** to accumulate **more sodium chloride** ions in the medulla. This means their medullas have especially **low water potentials** so **more** water can be reabsorbed from the collecting ducts, making their urine more concentrated.

Practice Questions

Q1 What are the main ways in which water can be lost from the body of a terrestrial animal?
Q2 Describe how the loop of Henle increases the salt concentration of the medulla of the kidney.
Q3 What is the effect of ADH on kidney function?

Exam Questions

Q1 Levels of ADH in the blood rise during strenuous exercise.
Explain the cause of the increase and the effects it has on kidney function. [10 marks]

Q2 Suggest why mammals adapted to life in dry deserts have longer loops of Henle. [5 marks]

If you don't understand what ADH does, urine trouble...

Seriously, though, there are two main things to learn from these pages — the countercurrent multiplier mechanism and the role of ADH in controlling the water content of urine. You'll need to be able to identify the different parts of the kidney nephron too. Keep writing it down until you've got it sorted in your head, and you'll be just fine.

Gas Exchange Surfaces

Many organisms have developed adaptations that enable them to exchange gases efficiently. Insects and plants always have to make a compromise between the need for respiratory gases and problems with water loss.

Gas exchange surfaces have **Four** Major **Adaptations**

Most gas exchange surfaces have four things in common:

1) They have a **large surface area** to **volume** ratio.

2) They are **thin** — often they're just one layer of epithelial cells.

3) There are **short diffusion pathways** between the gases and the internal tissues.

4) **Steep concentration gradients** between the tissues where gases are absorbed are maintained.

Organisms that have a blood transport system have a good capillary supply to gas exchange surfaces.

Fick's Law is used to Calculate **Diffusion Rates**

The rate at which a substance diffuses can be worked out using **Fick's law**:

$$\text{rate of diffusion} \propto \frac{\text{surface area} \times \text{difference in concentration}}{\text{thickness of membrane}}$$

$\propto$ means "is proportional to"

The body surface of a **Protoctist** is **Adapted** to its **Environment**

Protoctists are small, soft bodied, unicellular organisms which evolved around 1.5 billion years ago. There are about 60,000 protoctistan species all of which are aquatic. Algae are immobile, autotrophic protoctists and protozoa are heterotrophic protoctists.

Protoctists are well adapted to aquatic environments which only contain around **1% oxygen** —

1) They have all the usual features for efficient gas exchange — a **large, thin surface**, and an ability to maintain **high concentration gradients**.

2) The **short diffusion pathway** in **unicellular** organisms means that oxygen can take part in **biochemical reactions** as soon as it has **diffused** into the cell — there is **no need** for a circulatory system.

Fish are **Adapted** to live in an **Aquatic Environment**

The gills of a fish are a bit like the lungs of a mammal, except lungs are inward penetrating sacs and gills are **outward projecting filaments**. Gill filaments, called **lamellae**, increase the surface area for diffusion in just the same way that **alveoli** do in the lungs. The walls of gill lamellae are also made from very thin **squamous epithelium** to minimise the diffusion distance. A **blood system** carries gases between the **gaseous exchange surface** and the respiring **cells** — there are many **capillaries**, which carry blood **close** to the **surface** of the **gill lamellae**.

Water constantly flows over the gills and oxygen diffuses into the blood — that's because oxygen is more concentrated in the water than in the blood inside the capillaries. Some of the fastest moving fish have a **counter current system** where the blood and the water flow in opposite directions. The advantage of a counter current system is that it maintains a **high concentration gradient** of oxygen between the water and the blood.

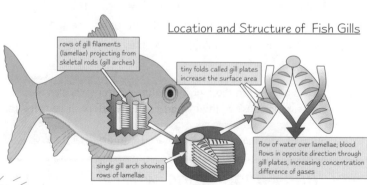

Location and Structure of Fish Gills

rows of gill filaments (lamellae) projecting from skeletal rods (gill arches)

tiny folds called gill plates increase the surface area

single gill arch showing rows of lamellae

flow of water over lamellae; blood flows in opposite direction through gill plates, increasing concentration difference of gases

The counter current method allows 90% of the available oxygen in the water to diffuse into the blood.

Gas Exchange Surfaces

Insects use **Tracheae** to **Exchange Gases**

Insects deal with gaseous exchange by having microscopic air-filled pipes called **tracheae** which penetrate the whole of the body from pores on the surface called **spiracles**. The tracheae branch off into smaller **tracheoles** which have **thin**, **permeable walls** and go to individual cells. This means that oxygen diffuses directly into the respiring cells — there's no need for a circulatory system. Insects use **rhythmic abdominal movements** to move air in and out of the spiracles.

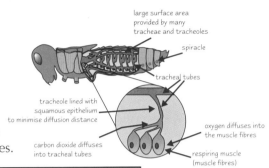

Plants exchange gases at the surface of the **Mesophyll Cells**

Plants exchange gases during respiration and photosynthesis. The main gas exchange surface is the surface of the mesophyll cells in the leaf. This is well adapted for its function — there's a large surface area.

The mesophyll cells are inside the leaf. Gases pass back and forth from the outside through special pores in the epidermis called stomata (singular = stoma). The stomata can open to allow exchange of gases, and close if the plant is losing too much water.

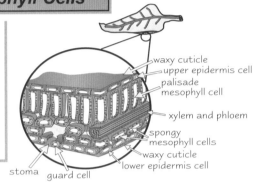

Insects and **Plants** can **Control Water Loss**

The problem with openings like stomata and spiracles that are designed to allow gases in and out is that they can lead to **water loss**. Plants and insects have **adaptations** which prevent dehydration:

1) **Insects** have muscles that they can use to **close** their **spiracles** if they are losing too much water. They also have tiny hairs around their spiracles which reduce evaporation.

2) In plants, the stomata are usually kept **open** to allow **gaseous exchange** (see page 45). **Proton pumps** in the guard cells pump **H⁺** ions **out** of them. This opens **potassium channels**, allowing K⁺ ions to enter the guard cells. This **lowers** their **water potential** and so water enters the guard cells by **osmosis**, which **opens** the stomata.

3) If the plant starts to get **dehydrated**, high light levels and temperatures cause **abscisic acid** to be released. This **stops** the proton pump working and so no water enters the guard cells by **osmosis**, the guard cells become **flaccid** and the **pore closes**.

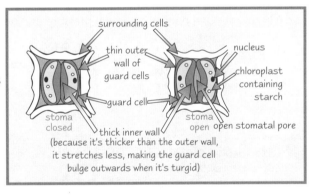

Practice Questions

Q1 What are the four essential adaptations for efficient gas exchange systems?
Q2 What is the equation for Fick's Law?
Q3 How are protoctists adapted for efficient gas exchange?
Q4 Describe how insects and plants stop excess water loss through gas exchange surfaces.

Exam Question

Q1 Using Fick's Law, predict whether the values of these three variables will be high or low when the rate of diffusion through the membrane is at its maximum:
a) surface area   b) difference in concentration   c) thickness in membrane.   [3 marks]

<u>Learn the principles — they apply to fish, plants and insects</u>

Once you've learnt those principles at the top of page 56 , you'll have a really good basis for understanding the rest of the stuff. Don't you think that it's pretty amazing that organisms as different as plants, fish and insects have evolved to use the same mechanisms to get the gases they need and get rid of the ones that they don't? No, I didn't think you would.

Transport of Respiratory Gases

Hmm, so how exactly does blood transport oxygen and carbon dioxide?

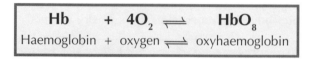

'Affinity' for oxygen means <u>willingness to combine</u> with oxygen.

Oxygen is Carried Around the Body as *Oxyhaemoglobin*

Oxygen is carried around the body by **haemoglobin** (Hb), in red blood cells. When oxygen joins to it, it becomes **oxyhaemoglobin**. This is a **reversible reaction** — when oxygen leaves oxyhaemoglobin (dissociates from it), it turns back to haemoglobin.

1) **Haemoglobin** is a large, **globular protein** molecule made up of four polypeptide chains.

2) Each chain has a **haem group** which contains **iron** and gives haemoglobin its **red** colour.

3) Haemoglobin has a **high affinity for oxygen** — each molecule carries **four oxygen molecules**.

$$Hb + 4O_2 \rightleftharpoons HbO_8$$
Haemoglobin + oxygen $\rightleftharpoons$ oxyhaemoglobin

Partial Pressure Measures *Concentration* of *Gases*

The **partial pressure of oxygen** (pO_2) is a measure of **oxygen concentration**.
The **greater** the concentration of dissolved oxygen in cells, the **higher** the partial pressure.
Similarly, the **partial pressure of carbon dioxide** (pCO_2) is a measure of the concentration of carbon dioxide in a cell.

> Where there's a **high pO_2**, oxygen **loads onto** haemoglobin to form oxyhaemoglobin.
> Where there has been a **decrease in pO_2**, oxyhaemoglobin **unloads** its oxygen.

1) Oxygen enters blood capillaries at the **alveoli** in the **lungs**. Alveoli cells have a **high pO_2** so oxygen **loads onto** haemoglobin to form oxyhaemoglobin.

2) When our **cells respire**, they use up oxygen. This **lowers pO_2**, so red blood cells deliver oxyhaemoglobin to respiring tissues, where it unloads its oxygen.

3) The haemoglobin then returns to the lungs to pick up more oxygen.

Dissociation Curves show how *Affinity for Oxygen* Varies

Dissociation curves show how the ability of haemoglobin to combine with oxygen varies, depending on partial pressure of oxygen (pO_2).

100% saturation means every haemoglobin molecule is carrying the maximum of 4 molecules of oxygen.

0% saturation means none of the haemoglobin molecules are carrying any oxygen.

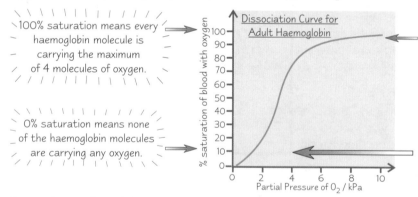

Where **pO_2 is high** (e.g. in the lungs), haemoglobin has a **high affinity** for oxygen (i.e. it will **readily combine** with oxygen), so it has a **high saturation** of oxygen.

Where **pO_2 is low** (e.g. in respiring tissues), haemoglobin has a **low affinity** for oxygen, which means it **releases oxygen** rather than combines with it. That's why it has a **low saturation** of oxygen.

The graph is 'S-shaped' because when haemoglobin (Hb) combines with the **first O_2 molecule**, it **alters the shape** of the Hb molecule in a way that makes it **easier** for other molecules to join too. But as the haemoglobin starts to become fully saturated, it becomes harder for more oxygen to join. As a result, the curve has a **steep** bit in the middle where it's really easy for oxygen molecules to join, and **shallow** bits at each end where it's harder for oxygen molecules to join.

Carbon Dioxide is transported to the *Lungs* as *Sodium Hydrogencarbonate*

1) Carbon dioxide is a waste product of respiration. CO_2 diffuses into red blood cells where the enzyme **carbonic anhydrase** converts it into **carbonic acid** by combining it with water.

2) Carbonic acid then **dissociates** into **hydrogencarbonate ions** (HCO_3^-) and **hydrogen** ions (H^+). The hydrogen ions cause oxyhaemoglobin to **dissociate** and the oxygen **diffuses** into the **cells** for **respiration**.

3) The HCO_3^- ions are pumped through the red blood cell membrane into the plasma where they combine with sodium to form **sodium hydrogencarbonate**. To make sure that the red blood cells remain electrically neutral, chloride ions pass into the red blood cells — this is known as the **chloride shift**.

4) The sodium hydrogencarbonate ions are carried in the **plasma** to the lungs where they combine with a **H^+ ion** and form **H_2O** and **CO_2**. The CO_2 is released during expiration.

Transport of Respiratory Gases

Carbon Dioxide Levels Affect Oxygen Unloading

To complicate matters, haemoglobin gives up its oxygen **more readily** at **higher partial pressures of carbon dioxide** (pCO_2). It's a cunning way of getting more oxygen to cells during activity. When cells respire more they produce more carbon dioxide, which raises pCO_2, increasing the rate of oxygen unloading.

The reason for this is linked to how CO_2 affects blood pH:

1) Remember from the previous page... CO_2 from respiration enters red blood cells, is converted to carbonic acid and then dissociates to give **hydrogen ions** and **hydrogencarbonate ions**.

2) Hydrogen ions combine with the haemoglobin, displacing oxygen and forming **haemoglobinic acid**.

3) This means that more oxygen is offloaded and the haemoglobin molecules act as **buffers, mopping up** H+ and preventing changes in pH.

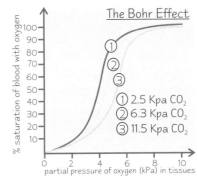

When carbon dioxide levels increase, the dissociation curve 'shifts' to the right, showing that more oxygen is released from the blood (because the lower the saturation of O_2 in blood, the more O_2 is being released). This is called the Bohr effect.

Haemoglobin is Not the Same in All Animals

The **chemical composition** of haemoglobin and its **oxygen carrying capacity** is different in different species.

Organisms that live in environments where little oxygen is available have dissociation curves to the **left** of human ones.

Organisms that are active and have large available oxygen supplies have curves which are to the **right** of the human one.

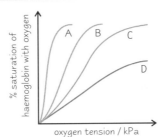

A = animal living in depleted oxygen environment e.g. a lugworm.

B = an animal living at high altitude where the partial pressure of oxygen is lower e.g. a llama living in the Andes.

C = a human dissociation curve.

D = an active animal with a high respiratory rate where there is plenty of available oxygen e.g. a hawk.

Practice Questions

Q1 Describe how haemoglobin carries oxygen.
Q2 Does haemoglobin have a high or low affinity for oxygen? What does 'affinity' mean?
Q3 What is the Bohr effect?
Q4 Name an organism that has an oxygen dissocation curve that is to the right of the human one.

Exam Question

Q1 Look at the graph below. It shows an oxygen dissociation curve for a human.
a) Draw a line on the graph to represent the dissociation curve of a pigeon. Label the line with a Y. [1 mark]
b) Draw a line on the graph to represent the dissociation curve of a yak, an animal that lives at high altitude. Label the line with an X. [1 mark]

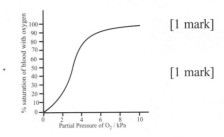

I have an affinity for fruit pastilles...

Dissociation graphs are definitely confusing — it's hard to imagine what's going on. The thing to remember is that when tissues contain lots of oxygen (i.e. the partial pressure is high), haemoglobin readily combines with oxygen, so the blood gets saturated with oxygen. When the partial pressure is low, oxygen moves from the blood into the tissues.

Digestion and Absorption

Time for a bit of blood and guts — well, actually, mainly just the guts. The human digestive system demands respect — it's an amazing bit of kit that has to deal with whatever you trough. It's no coincidence that 'gutsy' means well 'ard.

The **Gut Wall** Consists of **Four Layers** of Tissue

The gut wall has the same **general structure** all the way through the human gut:

1) The **mucosa** (inner lining) lubricates the passage of food with **mucus**. This prevents **autodigestion** (enzymes attacking the gut wall). It's lined with **surface epithelium** cells.

2) The **submucosa** contains capillary beds and nerve fibres.

3) The **circular and longitudinal muscles** control the shape and movement of the gut.

4) The **serosa** contains tough tissue, which provides protection from friction against other organs.

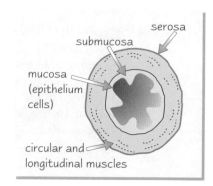

The **Gut Wall** is **Adapted** for its **Functions**

As you move down the alimentary canal the structure of the gut wall changes so that it can perform particular jobs effectively (there's more about the different parts of the gut on pages 62-63).

The gut wall in the **oesophagus** uses it's circular and longitudinal muscles to perform **peristalsis**. These muscles work as an **antagonistic pair** — as one contracts, the other relaxes. Food is pushed along in front of the contractions.

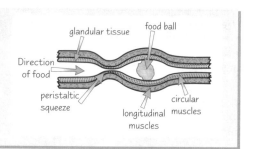

The mucosa in the **stomach** contains **gastric pits**, which secrete gastric juice (see p 62 for more on gastric juice).

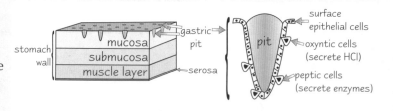

The mucosa in the **ileum** (small intestine) has **villi** and **microvilli** to **increase the surface area** for absorbing the products of digestion. It also has other adaptations for effective absorption:

- It consists of a **single layer** of epithelial cells, so there's a **short diffusion pathway**.
- A **moist lining** helps substances **dissolve** so they can pass through cell membranes.
- The **capillary bed** takes away **absorbed molecules** so the diffusion gradient is maintained.
- **Lymph vessels** take away absorbed **glycerol** and **fatty acids** to join the lymphatic system. This maintains the diffusion gradient.
- **Carrier proteins** in epithelial cell membranes allow **facilitated diffusion**.
- The epithelial cells contain lots of **mitochondria** to make ATP, needed for **active transport**.

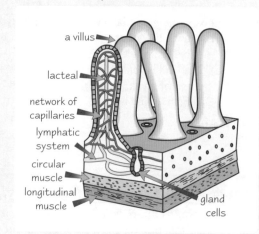

Digestion and Absorption

Ruminants can digest Cellulose

Cellulose is a major component of vegetation (it forms the cell walls). Because plant material generally has a low nutritional value it is important that herbivorous animals can access the **nutrients** and **energy** in the **cellulose**.
Ruminants are herbivores that have **four stomach sections** and specialised teeth to grind up plant materials — deer, giraffes, antelopes, cattle, sheep and goats are all ruminants.

1) Ruminants use **incisors** (large teeth at the front of the mouth) to crop vegetation.

2) The first section of the stomach, the reticulum, forms balls of **cud** from the swallowed material.

3) The animal **regurgitates** this cud and chews it again to break it down mechanically. Ruminants have a special horny pad inside their mouth which they use with their premolars and molars to mash the cud.

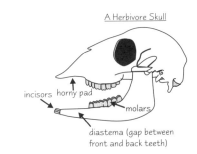
A Herbivore Skull

incisors horny pad
molars
diastema (gap between front and back teeth)

4) When the ruminant swallows again, the food bypasses the reticulum. It gradually makes its way through the next three sections of the stomach — the **rumen**, the **omasum** and the **abomasum**. The rumen is the largest part of the stomach and it contains millions of **mutualistic microorganisms** that **ferment** the vegetation in **anaerobic conditions** — it's these bacteria that break down the cellulose.

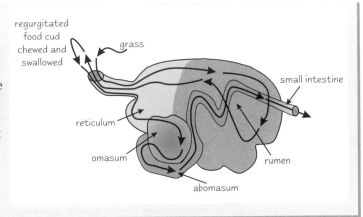
regurgitated food cud chewed and swallowed
grass
reticulum
omasum
rumen
abomasum
small intestine

5) When the microorganisms **die** they pass into the ruminant's **small intestine** where they are broken down and absorbed providing sugars, vitamins and **amino acids**. The amino acids are broken down **proteins** that are made from **ammonia** that microorganisms secrete into the fluid in the reticulum.

Practice Questions

Q1 Name the four layers of the gut wall.
Q2 Draw the layers of the gut wall, label them and describe the functions.
Q3 What is peristalsis?
Q4 What do gastric pits secrete?
Q5 Name three ruminants.
Q6 Name the four sections of a ruminant's stomach.

Exam Question

Q1 Describe how the gut wall in the ileum is adapted for its function. [6 marks]

There's urea in cow food...

Honestly, they put it in because it's a source of nitrogen for the bacteria in the rumen. Well anyway, I don't actually think these pages are too bad — there's not too much to learn and some of it will probably be familiar from when you did GCSE. The stuff about ruminants should be OK too. Just make sure you learn all the little details and you'll be fine.

Digestion and Absorption

Well, food goes in one end, and it comes out of the other. You'd think that's pretty simple but I'm afraid those examiners have set about making it as complicated as they can...

Each Part of the **Digestive System** has a **Specific Function**

Animals are **heterotrophic** (they can't make their own food like plants so they feed on other living material), they **ingest** (eat) their food, **digest** it (break it down into smaller molecules), **absorb** it, and **egest** any wastes as faeces.

Each part of the **digestive system** has a **role** in **breaking down** food and **absorbing** its **nutrients**:

The Mouth

In the **mouth**, **mastication** (chewing) of food by teeth **mechanically** breaks up food so there's a **larger surface area** for enzymes to work on. Mixing food with saliva (water, **amylase** and mucus) partly digests food so it can be swallowed easily. The amylase **hydrolyses** starch into maltose.

The Oesophagus

The oesophagus is a tube that takes food from the mouth to the **stomach** using **peristalsis** (see p60). **Mucus** is secreted from glandular tissue in the walls, to **lubricate** the food's passage downwards.

The Stomach

The stomach is a small sac beneath the diaphragm. It can hold up to 4 litres of food and liquid — it has many folds which expand when there is lots of food. The entrance and exit of the stomach are controlled by **sphincter muscles**. **Gastric juice** produced by the stomach walls is responsible for chemical digestion. **Gastric juice** consists of hydrochloric acid (HCl), **pepsinogen** (which is then converted into the enzyme **pepsin**) and mucus. Pepsin is an **endopeptidase** — it hydrolyses peptide bonds in the **middle** of polypeptide molecules (proteins), breaking them down into smaller polypeptide chains (which gives a larger surface area for **exopeptidases** to work on later on in digestion). It only works in **acidic conditions**, which are provided by the HCl. **Peristalsis** of the stomach turns food into an acidic fluid, called **chyme**.

The Small Intestine

The small intestine has two main parts — the **duodenum** and the **ileum**. Chyme is moved along the small intestine via peristalsis.

In the **duodenum**, alkaline bile and pancreatic juice **neutralise** the **acidity** of the chyme.

- Bile is produced in the **liver** and stored in the **gall bladder**, then it enters the duodenum through the **bile duct**. It **emulsifies** lipids into small droplets, which speeds up hydrolysis of lipids by **pancreatic lipase** (there's more about the pancreas on the next page).

- **Pancreatic juice** contains the digestive **enzymes lipase, amylase, trypsinogen** (which is converted into **trypsin**) and **exopeptidases** (see the table on the opposite page). Exopeptidases hydrolyse peptide bonds found at the end of polypeptide chains, giving free **amino acids**. There are also **endopeptidases** which break bonds in the **middle** of polypeptides giving shorter polypeptides which are then broken into single amino acids by **dipeptidases**.

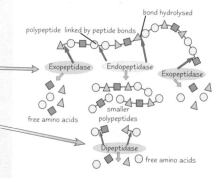

- **Intestinal juice** is produced by the gut wall. It contains more digestive **enzymes** — more lipases, maltase, exopeptidases and dipeptidases.

In the **ileum** the small, soluble molecules of digested food (glucose, amino acids, fatty acids and glycerol) are **absorbed** through the **microvilli** lining the gut wall. Absorption is through diffusion, facilitated diffusion and active transport.

Digestion and Absorption

The Pancreas

The pancreas is an organ which acts as a gland releasing **pancreatic juice** into the duodenum via the **pancreatic duct**. Pancreatic juice is produced by the epithelial cells which line the ducts in the pancreas. Pancreatic juice contains **amylase**, **trypsin**, the endopeptidase **chymotrypsin**, and **lipase** (the functions of these chemicals are listed below). Pancreatic juice also contains **sodium bicarbonate** which neutralises the acidity of the hydrochloric acid from the stomach.

The Colon

The colon (large intestine) absorbs **water**, **salts** and **minerals** — like the other parts of the digestive system the colon has a **folded wall** to provide a **large surface area** for absorption. In the colon bacteria decompose some of the leftover nutrients. Faeces are stored in the rectum and then pass through **sphincter** muscles at the **anus** during **defaecation**.

Enzymes *and* Digestive Juices *have different functions*

You need to know all the information in this table for the exam:

	site of production	site of action	function
amylase	salivary gland	mouth	starch to maltose
pepsin	stomach	stomach	protein to polypeptides
amylase	pancreas	duodenum	starch to maltose
bile salts	liver (stored in the gall bladder)	duodenum	emulsify fats and neutralise the acidity of chyme
lipase	pancreas	duodenum	fats to fatty acids and glycerol
maltase	duodenal glands	duodenum	maltose to glucose
trypsin	pancreas	duodenum	protein to polypeptides
chymotrypsin	pancreas	duodenum	protein to polypeptides
endopeptidases	stomach, pancreas	stomach, duodenum	long polypeptides to shorter ones
exopeptidases	pancreas, duodenal glands	duodenum	short polypeptides to amino acids
dipeptidases	duodenal glands	duodenum	double amino acids to single ones

It's a bit weird that sometimes two chemicals do the same thing but it's true.

Learning this table is a good way of getting your head round digestion — it basically summarises the ways that your body breaks down protein, starch and fat.

Practice Questions

Q1 What do these words mean: a) ingest   b) mastication?

Q2 Explain the structure and function of the stomach.

Q3 What is the purpose of the intestinal juice that is produced by the gut wall?

Q4 Name three chemicals in pancreatic juice.

Exam Questions

Q1 Explain how protein is broken down in the digestive system. [4 marks]

Q2 Name 6 digestive enzymes and their functions. [6 marks]

My mum told me mastication would make me go blind

Quite a bit to learn here — it's understandable, 'cos digestion is a complicated process with many stages. The key thing is to learn what each bit of the gut does and how it's adapted to do this function. Make sure you know the difference between endo and exopeptidases. Then eat some food, and revise it its passage down the body, not lingering on the last stage though.

Control of Digestive Secretions

Once you eat some food, digestion isn't just a passive process — the unconsciously controlled parts of your body are busy making sure it's all working efficiently all the time.

Two Systems are involved in Controlling Digestion

Digestion is controlled by both the **nervous** and **hormonal** systems. They can work **together** to bring about certain effects, for example, nervous impulses can cause hormones to be secreted.

1) The **hormones** that control digestion are **gastrin, secretin** and **cholecystokinin-pancreozymin** — they're released by cells in the **mucosa** of the **stomach** and **small intestine**. These hormones are only released when food is present in the digestive system.

2) **Two types of nerves** help to control the digestive system — **extrinsic and intrinsic nerves**.

Extrinsic and Intrinsic Nerves do different jobs in the Digestive System

Extrinsic Nerves

Extrinsic nerves come to the digestive organs from the subconscious part of the brain and spinal cord. The chemical transmitters **acetylcholine** and **adrenaline** are released across the synapses. Acetylcholine **increases** the muscle action in the stomach and intestines and **increases** the production of **digestive juices** and **enzymes**. **Adrenaline inhibits** the muscles of the digestive system.

Intrinsic nerves

Intrinsic nerves are triggered to act when the walls of the digestive organs are **stretched**. Intrinsic nerves trigger the release of **hormones** and **digestive juices**.

Remember that the three sites where digestive chemicals are secreted are the mouth, the stomach and the small intestine.

Food can bring about Simple or Conditioned Reflexes

Reflexes are **rapid** responses to the presence of food that are controlled by the **autonomic nervous system** (ANS see p. 76-77).

Conditioned reflexes are ones that are **learnt** through **association**. For example, you learn to associate certain **stimuli** like the **sight** and **smell** of food with eating. These **stimuli** trigger **receptors** in the eyes and nose which send **nerve impulses** to the brain. The **sympathetic** nervous system (see p. 76-77) then sends **impulses** via the **vagus nerve** to the salivary glands, stomach and gall bladder and **saliva, gastric juice** and **bile** are released in **anticipation** of food.

Ivan Pavlov first researched conditioned reflexes by experimenting on dogs.

The thought or taste of food stimulates nerve impulses that control the release of gastric juices in the stomach. About 200cm³ of gastric juices are released. When the food arrives in the stomach over 600cm³ of gastric juices are released. There are about 40 million cells in the stomach lining which release a total of 2 – 3 dm³ of gastric juice per day.

Simple reflexes are the ones that can't be controlled and aren't learnt — they happen **subconsciously**. Simple reflexes are controlled by the **parasympathetic** nervous system.

1) The presence of **food** in the **mouth** sends nervous impulses (via the central nervous system) to the **stomach** bringing about the release of gastric juice.

2) The presence of food in the **stomach** stretches the walls and stimulates the **release** of **HCl**.

3) The **autonomic nervous system** brings about a simple reflex in the stomach which causes **peristalsis** (waves of muscular contraction) in the **small intestine**. This moves the food along making room for **chyme** to be **released** from the stomach.

Control of Digestive Secretions

Three Hormones are released in the Digestive System

1) **Gastrin** release is stimulated by food **distending** (expanding) the stomach wall. Gastrin brings about the secretion of **hydrochloric acid**.

2) **Cholecystokinin pancreozymin** (CCK-PZ) is released by the presence of **fatty food** in the **small intestine** — it stimulates bile to be released from the gall bladder. It also increases the amount of digestive **enzymes** that the **pancreas** releases.

3) **Secretin** is released when **chyme** reaches the duodenum. Secretin stimulates the pancreas to release **hydrogencarbonate ions** which neutralise stomach acid. Secretin also stimulates bile production in the liver.

There are differences between Nervous Control and Hormonal Control

In the digestive system, the **nervous impulses** and the **hormones** work together to stimulate both fast and slow reactions to the food received in the body:

Hormonal Control

The hormonal system works by releasing **chemicals**, which are carried in the blood, from **glands**. Hormones take some **time** to work, but their effects last a relatively **long time**. Hormones act in fairly general ways, e.g. a single hormone might bring about several different responses.

These differences between hormonal and nervous control don't just apply to the digestive system — they're important throughout the whole of biology.

Nervous Control

The nervous system uses **chemical transmitters** that create **electrical impulses** and transmit information. These impulses are **quick-acting** and have a **short-lived** effect. One of the main jobs of the nervous system in digestion is to stimulate the release of **hormones**. It also controls **muscular activities** like peristalsis. Nervous impulses are very **specific** — e.g. some act on **single** muscle fibres.

Practice Questions

Q1 Where are gastrin and secretin released?
Q2 What is the difference between the extrinsic and intrinsic nerves that affect the digestive system?
Q3 Describe how a conditioned reflex brings about the release of saliva.
Q4 Which nervous system are simple reflexes controlled by?
Q5 What role do the following hormones play in the digestive system? a) gastrin b) CCK-PZ c) secretin

Exam Questions

Q1 Describe the ways that the nervous system acts upon the digestive system. [5 marks]

Q2 State whether each of the following are brought about nervously or hormonally.
(Some answers may be a combination of the above).
a) secretion of gastric juices
b) production of saliva
c) stimulation of release of bile [3 marks]

Cholecystokinin pancreozymin — just rolls off the tongue, doesn't it...

Other than that these pages aren't too bad really. Make sure that you've got the hang of the differences between nervous and hormonal control of the digestive system. And remember that there are two kinds of nerves — intrinsic and extrinsic, and two kinds of reflexes — simple and conditioned.

Metamorphosis and Insect Diet

Metamorphosis in insects happens when they take on different forms. You need to learn the example of lepidopterous insects (butterflies and moths) for the exam.

A **Lepidopterous Insect** has more than one **Body Form**

Lepidopterous insects have life cycles that go through **four stages**:

1) An adult lays an **egg**.
2) The egg hatches into a **caterpillar** or **larva**.
3) The caterpillar forms the **chrysalis** or **pupa** (pupation).
4) The caterpillar hatches into a **butterfly** or a **moth** (imago).

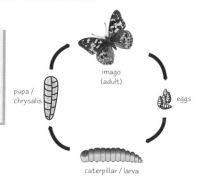

Eggs are laid on **Plants**

1) The eggs are laid by the **female** on a **plant** that will provide **food** for the caterpillar.
2) The parent butterfly recognises the plant according to its **shape**, **colour** and **chemical composition**.
3) Once the eggs are laid they are **abandoned** by the parent.
4) A caterpillar (larva) emerges after about 5 days.

Caterpillars **Eat a Lot**

1) A newly emerged caterpillar has a **segmented body** consisting of a **head** with **biting jaws**, a **thorax** with **three** pairs of **jointed legs** with hooks, and an **abdomen** with **five** pairs of stumpy **prolegs**. Caterpillars have simple eyes (ocelli) which only detect changes in light.

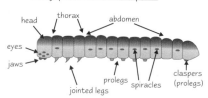

Body parts of a caterpillar

2) Caterpillars have **powerful jaws** (mandibles) that have sharp cutting surfaces. The jaws also have two **maxillae** which guide food into the mouth. The maxillae also contain chemical detectors which enable the caterpillar to identify appropriate food.

3) Most caterpillars live for up to a month and they **eat** constantly. As caterpillars grow they **shed** their skins (**ecdysis**) — three or four moultings take place before a chrysalis or pupa is formed. Caterpillars use **silk** thread made in their **silk glands** to attach themselves onto a plant.

The **Pupa Stage** usually lasts for about **Three Weeks**

Inside the chrysalis all the tissues are broken down into a **liquid**. The only parts that aren't dissolved are the **central nervous system** and some special groups of cells called **imaginal discs**. The **adult** (butterfly / moth) **organs** are formed from the imaginal discs. Some species spend **winter** as pupae to avoid harsh weather conditions.

Eventually, the skin of the chrysalis splits and a butterfly / moth **emerges**. Butterflies / moths have **compound eyes** which are more complex than the ocelli that caterpillars have. They also have a long straw-like tube called a **proboscis** that they use for feeding on **nectar**. Butterflies and moths always have **six legs**. Once they have emerged the adults **don't grow**.

Metamorphosis and Insect Diet

Different stages have different **Nutritional Requirements**

The **different stages** in the **life cycle** of a lepidopterous insect have different **nutritional requirements**. For example, caterpillars need lots of protein because they are growing, whilst butterflies need lots of carbohydrate to provide energy for flying. The insects also have different **adaptations** to allow them to feed during different life stages —

	egg / embryo
source of food	yolk contains protein, phospholipids and fats
protein / energy requirements	rapid development requires high levels of energy and protein
mouthparts / digestive structures	mandibles grow as it develops
gut enzymes	peptidases, lipase
	caterpillar
source of food	leaves
protein / energy requirements	protein needed for growth, carbohydrate needed for energy
mouthparts / digestive structures	mandibles and maxillae
gut enzymes	peptidases, cellulase, amylase
	pupa
source of food	none
protein / energy requirements	uses stored energy for metamorphosis
mouthparts / digestive structures	none
gut enzymes	none
	butterfly / moth
source of food	nectar
protein / energy requirements	high energy requirement for flying
mouthparts / digestive structures	proboscis
gut enzymes	sucrase

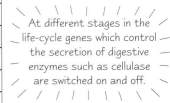

At different stages in the life-cycle genes which control the secretion of digestive enzymes such as cellulase are switched on and off.

Practice Questions

Q1 What are the four stages in the life of a lepidopterous insect?

Q2 Describe how caterpillars eat.

Q3 Describe the physical structure of a caterpillar.

Q4 What happens during pupation?

Q5 How does a lepidopterous insect feed when it is a butterfly?

Exam Questions

Q1 Name the different digestive enzymes needed at each of the four life stages of a swallowtail butterfly. [6 marks]

Q2 What are: a) mandibles b) imaginal discs c) maxillae? [3 marks]

I'm glad that my insides never liquefy

Well, as improbable as all this sounds, it is true. If you think back to section two, having different life-stages feeding on different foods is advantageous because it reduces intra-specific competition. Remember that this stuff applies to all lepidopterous insects, so don't be put off if they ask you about one particular species of butterfly — just apply what you've learnt here and you'll be fine.

Neurones

Neurones are long cells that carry information around your body as electrical impulses. They're fascinating. Honest.

Nerve Cells have Polarised Membranes so they can carry Electrical Signals

1) The **nervous system** is made up of nerve cells called **neurones**. Each neurone consists of a **cell body** and extending **nerve fibres**, which are very thin cylinders of cytoplasm bound by a cell membrane. Neurones carry waves of electrical activity called **action potentials** (nerve impulses). They can carry these impulses because their cell membranes are **polarised** (see below) — there are different **charges** on the inside and outside of the membrane.

2) The nerve fibres let the neurones carry action potentials over **long distances**. There are tiny gaps, called **synapses**, between the different nerve fibres. Action potentials can't cross, so a chemical called a **neurotransmitter** is secreted at the tip of each nerve fibre to cross the gap. This stimulates a **new** action potential in the next nerve fibre on the other side of the synapse (see pages 70-71).

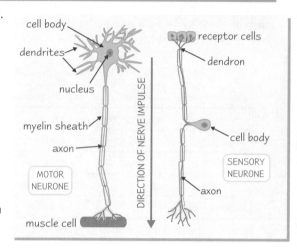

3) Between the receptors and the effectors, the **central nervous system** (i.e. brain and spinal cord) **coordinates** the action potentials passing through the nervous system. **Sensory neurones** carry action potentials from receptors to the central nervous system. **Relay neurones** carry action potentials through the central nervous system, and **motor (effector) neurones** carry them from the central nervous system to effectors.

Neurone cell membranes are Polarised when they're Resting

Resting neurones have a **potential difference** (a difference in **charge**) of about **-65 millivolts** (mV) across their cell membranes. This is because the **outer** surface of the membrane is **positively** charged and the **inner** surface **negatively** charged — the -65 mV is the **overall difference** in charge between them. This is the **resting potential** of the membrane, which is said to be **polarised**.

The resting potential is generated by a **sodium-potassium pump** and a **potassium channel** in the membrane. The sodium-potassium pump moves **three sodium ions** out of the cell by **active transport** for every **two potassium ions** it brings in. The potassium channel then allows **facilitated diffusion** of potassium ions back out of the cell. The outer surface of the membrane becomes more positive than the inner surface because overall, more positive ions move **out** of the cell than move **in**.

Sodium-potassium pump and potassium channel

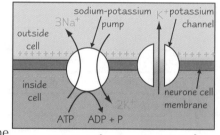

movement of potassium/sodium ions by active transport

movement of potassium ions by diffusion

Neurone cells become Depolarised when they're Stimulated

The **sodium-potassium pumps** work pretty much all the time, but **channel proteins** (like the potassium channels) can be opened or closed. **Depolarisation** of neurone cell membranes involves another type of channel protein, **sodium channels**. If a neurone cell membrane is stimulated, sodium channels **open** and **sodium ions** diffuse in. This **increases** the positive charge **inside** the cell, so the charge across the membrane is **reversed**. The membrane now carries a potential difference of about **+40 mV**. This is the **action potential** and the membrane is **depolarised**.

When sodium ions diffuse into the cell, this stimulates nearby bits of membrane and **more** sodium channels open. Once they've opened, the channels automatically **recover** and close again.

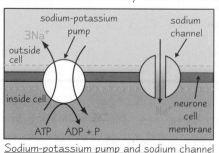

Sodium-potassium pump and sodium channel

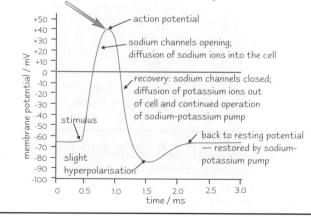

Neurones

Remember these important features of Action Potentials

1) **Nerve axons** in vertebrates are usually covered in a layer of **myelin sheath**, which is produced by **Schwann cells**. Myelin is an **electrical insulator**. Between the sheaths there are tiny patches of bare membrane called **nodes of Ranvier**, where sodium channels are **concentrated**. Action potentials **jump** from one node to another, which lets them move **faster** (this is called **saltatory conduction**).

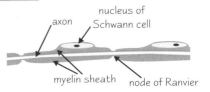

2) Action potentials also go faster along axons with **bigger diameters**, because there's less **electrical resistance**.

3) They go faster as **temperature** increases too, up to around **40°C**. After that, the proteins begin to **denature**.

4) Action potentials have an **all-or-nothing** nature. This means that the values of the resting and action potentials for a neurone are **constant**, and you can't get anything in between. (A **bigger stimulus** just increases the **frequency** of the action potentials. The **strength** of the action potentials stays the same.)

5) A **threshold stimulus** must be applied to get an action potential (see page 72).

6) Straight after an action potential has been generated, the membrane enters a short **refractory period** when it can't be stimulated, because the sodium channels are **recovering** and can't be opened. This makes the action potentials pass along as **separate signals**.

7) Action potentials are **unidirectional** — they can only pass in one direction.

Practice Questions

Q1 What do sensory, relay and motor neurones do in the nervous system?

Q2 What happens to sodium ions when a neurone membrane is stimulated?

Q3 Give two factors that increase the speed of conduction of action potentials.

Q4 What is meant by the 'all-or-nothing' nature of action potentials?

Exam Questions

Q1 The graph shows an action potential 'spike' across an axon membrane following the application of a stimulus.

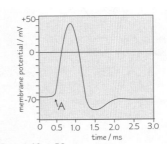

a) What label should be added at point A? [1 mark]

b) Explain what causes the change in potential difference from -65 to +40 mV. [3 marks]

c) Another stimulus was applied at 1.5 ms, but failed to produce an action potential. Suggest why. [2 marks]

Q2 Multiple sclerosis is a disease of the nervous system characterised by damaged myelin sheath. Suggest and explain how this will affect the transmission of action potentials. [5 marks]

I'm feeling a bit depolarised after all that...

The nervous system can seem like a really hard subject at first, but once you've gone over it a couple of times it starts to make sense. Nerves work because there's a charge across their membranes, and it's a change in this charge that sends the message along the nerve. The charge is set up using ions, which can then be pumped in and out to change the charge.

Synaptic Transmission

This page is all about synapses, which are the little gaps between the end of one neurone and the start of the next one. Seems like quite an insignificant little thing to fill a whole two pages with, but never mind.

There are Gaps between Neurones

A **synapse** is a gap between the end of one **neurone** and the start of the next. An action potential arrives at the end of the axon of the **presynaptic neurone** (the neurone before the synapse), where there's a swelling called a **bouton** or **synaptic knob**. This has **vesicles** containing a chemical **neurotransmitter**, and the impulse passes across the synapse as follows:

1) The action potential opens calcium channels in the membrane, allowing calcium ions to diffuse into the bouton. Afterwards these are pumped back out using ATP.

2) The increased concentration of calcium ions in the bouton causes the vesicles containing the neurotransmitter to move up to and to fuse with the presynaptic membrane. This also requires ATP (it's an active process).

3) The vesicles release their neurotransmitter into the synaptic cleft (this is called exocytosis and it's an active process too).

4) The neurotransmitter diffuses across the synaptic cleft and binds to receptors on the postsynaptic membrane of the other neurone.

5) This stimulates an action potential in the postsynaptic membrane by opening the sodium channels (see page 68).

6) An enzyme is sometimes used to hydrolyse the neurotransmitter, so the response doesn't keep on happening. The neurotransmitter may also be taken back up into the presynaptic bouton, ready to be used again.

Because the receptors are only on the **postsynaptic** membranes, a signal can only pass across a synapse in **one direction** (it's **unidirectional**). The postsynaptic cell behaves as a **transducer**, just like **receptor cells** (see page 72), because the **chemical** stimulus (neurotransmitter) is converted into an **electrical** one (action potential).

There are lots of **mitochondria** in the bouton of a neurone. These provide the **ATP** to make more neurotransmitter, power exocytosis and pump calcium ions out of the bouton.

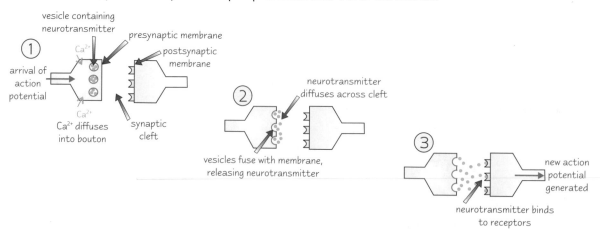

There's a Synapse between a Motor Neurone and Muscle Fibres

Motor neurones carry action potentials to **muscle fibres**. There's a synapse between the presynaptic membrane of the motor axon and the postsynaptic membrane of the muscle fibre (the **sarcolemma**). This region is called the **neuromuscular junction**. The synapse functions in the same way as a synapse between two neurones, and an action potential is generated on the sarcolemma in the same way too. This brings about a muscular contraction.

Synaptic Transmission

There are Different Kinds of Neurotransmitters

There are many kinds of neurotransmitters. A lot of neurotransmitters are **excitatory** (as described opposite), but some are **inhibitory**. These make the membrane **hyperpolarised**, creating a resting potential value that's even more **negative** than the usual -65 mV. This makes it harder to **excite**.

Some kinds of neurones in particular parts of the body, only have receptors for certain **types** of neurotransmitter, e.g:

1) The neurotransmitter **acetylcholine** binds to **cholinergic receptors**. It's an excitatory neurotransmitter at many neurones and neuromuscular junctions.

2) **Noradrenaline** binds to **adrenergic receptors**, and it's generally **excitatory**.

Some **drugs** and **poisons** affect the action of neurotransmitters:
- **Agonists** are chemicals that **mimic** the effects of neurotransmitters. An example is **nicotine**, which binds to **cholinergic** receptors and stimulates **neuromuscular junctions**.
- **Antagonists block** the effects of neurotransmitters. An example is **curare**, a chemical that binds to **cholinergic receptors**, but blocks – rather than mimics – the acetylcholine molecules. This **paralyses** the muscle.

Synapses are sites of Interaction between Different Signals

The main function of a synapse is to bring about the passage of signals between neurones. However, another important point about synapses is that signals can **interact** there:

1) **Inhibition.** A neurotransmitter can **inhibit** a postsynaptic membrane and make it harder to excite by **hyperpolarising** it.

2) **Summation.** This means that the **overall effect** of lots of different neurotransmitters from lots of different neurones on one postsynaptic membrane is the **sum** of all their **individual effects** (bearing in mind that some might be **excitatory** and some might be **inhibitory**).

Practice Questions

Q1 Why are there a lot of mitochondria in the bouton (synaptic knob) of the neurone?
Q2 Give two examples of a neurotransmitter.
Q3 Is nicotine an agonist or an antagonist at cholinergenic receptors?
Q4 What effect do antagonists have on neurotransmitters? Give an example of an antagonist.
Q5 What is summation at a synapse?

Exam Questions

Q1 Describe the sequence of events leading from the arrival of an action potential at a bouton to the generation of a new action potential on a post-synaptic membrane. [8 marks]
Q2 Explain how the structure of the synapse ensures that signals can only pass through it in one direction. [4 marks]

Bouton — like button, but in a weird French accent...

Not the most exciting page in the book, but pleasantly dull I'd say. There's nothing too hard there. Some chemicals with annoyingly long names cross a gap so action potentials can move from neurone to neurone through the body. You need to know the difference between agonists and antagonists for the exam too.

Receptors and the Reflex Arc

The nervous system is really important to animals. Plants don't have nervous systems at all, and that's why they tend to sit around doing nothing all day. Our nervous system lets us respond to our environment and tells us what's going on.

Organisms have **Receptors** that are sensitive to **Stimuli**

A **stimulus** is any change in the environment that brings about a **response** in an organism — for example, a vibration that's detected by receptors in an organism's ears as a sound, or light that's detected by receptors in the organism's eyes as an image. A **receptor** is the part of the body of an organism that **detects** the stimulus.

You can classify receptors in animals depending on the **type of stimulus** they detect:

1) **Thermoreceptors** are sensitive to temperature — they're stimulated by **heat energy**.

2) **Photoreceptors** are sensitive to **light** — they're stimulated by **electromagnetic energy**, e.g. the cells that contain the pigments in the retina of the eye.

3) **Mechanoreceptors** are sensitive to **sound**, **touch**, **pressure** or even **gravity** — they're stimulated by **kinetic energy**.

4) **Chemoreceptors** are sensitive to **chemicals** — they're stimulated by **chemical energy**. They're involved in the senses of smell and taste.

Receptor cells have **Excitable Membranes**

1) Receptor cells are **excitable**. This means that in their resting (unstimulated) state, their cell membranes have a **potential difference** across them — i.e. the receptor cells have a difference in **charge** across their cell membranes. There's a **negative** charge on the **inside** of the membrane, and a **positive** charge on the **outside**. This is generated by a combination of protein **ion pumps** and **channels** (see page 68).

2) When the receptor cell is stimulated, changes inside the cell affect the charge across the cell membrane. **Ions** (charged atoms) move into or out of the cell and alter the **charge** on each face of the membrane. Charges are **reversed**, creating a **generator potential**. The larger the stimulus, the larger the generator potential.

3) When the receptor cell is stimulated (**excited**) like this, it can transmit a signal to an **effector**, as long as the **generator potential** is big enough. Stimulated receptors that set up **nerve impulses** in nerve cells are called **transducers**.

4) The **minimum** size of stimulus needed to transmit a signal is called the **threshold stimulus**. Some kinds of receptor cells need a bigger stimulus than others to get a response (they have a **higher threshold**), so they're **less sensitive**.

A **Pacinian Corpuscle** is a **Skin Receptor**

The **skin** has lots of different types of **receptors**. Pacinian **corpuscles** detect **pressure** applied to the skin. When a corpuscle is deformed by something pushing on it, 'stretch-mediated' sodium channels in the cell membrane open. **Sodium ions** move into the cell by **facilitated diffusion**, creating a **generator potential**. Each Pacinian corpuscle contains a **sensory nerve ending** from a **sensory neurone**. When the **threshold stimulus** is reached, an **action potential** (nerve impulse) is set up in the membrane of the sensory neurone.

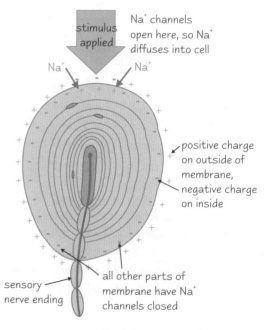

stimulus applied

Na$^+$ channels open here, so Na$^+$ diffuses into cell

Na$^+$ Na$^+$

positive charge on outside of membrane, negative charge on inside

sensory nerve ending

all other parts of membrane have Na$^+$ channels closed

Pacinian corpuscle

Tip no. 31: Pictures of pigs are great for disguising boring pages.

Receptors and the Reflex Arc

Effectors bring about a Response

An **effector** is a part of the body that brings about a **response** to the signal from a receptor.
In animals, effectors are usually **muscles** (the response is **contraction**), or **glands** (the response is **secretion**).

Reflex Arc Pathways communicate quickly with Effectors

A **reflex** is an **involuntary stereotypical** response of part of an organism to an applied stimulus. This means that there's usually no **conscious control** over it, and it always produces the **same** kind of effect. It works because there are special patterns of neurones that make up **reflex arcs**. The simplest is a **monosynaptic reflex**, where the sensory neurone connects **directly** to the motor neurone so there's only **one synapse** within the central nervous system in the arc. An example is the **knee jerk reflex**. These reflex arcs often play a role in controlling **muscle tone** and **maintaining posture**. Action potentials don't pass to the **brain**, and so no conscious thought is needed for them to happen.

A **polysynaptic reflex** has at least **two synapses** within the central nervous system, due to the presence of a **relay neurone**. Action potentials **can** pass to the brain, so some conscious thought might be involved. An example of such a reflex is the quick response if you touch something hot.

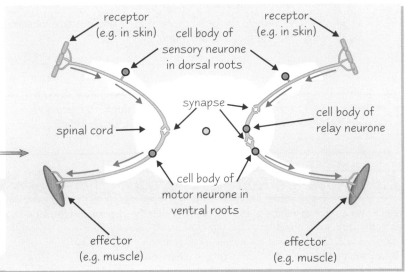

Ventral roots (bottom) and dorsal roots (top) are just the parts of spinal nerves that join with the spinal cord.

Transverse section through spinal cord showing monosynaptic reflex arc (left) and polysynaptic reflex arc (right)

receptor
(e.g. in skin)

cell body of
sensory neurone
in dorsal roots

receptor
(e.g. in skin)

synapse

cell body of
relay neurone

spinal cord

cell body of
motor neurone in
ventral roots

effector
(e.g. muscle)

effector
(e.g. muscle)

Practice Questions

Q1   Why is it important that organisms can respond to stimuli in their environment?

Q2   What do receptors and effectors do in the nervous system?

Q3   What kinds of energy stimulate mechanoreceptors and photoreceptors?

Q4   How does the potential difference change when a stimulus is applied?

Q5   What is the threshold level of a stimulus?

Q6   What is a reflex response?

Exam Question

Q1   Chemoreceptors detect chemical stimuli. Suggest why exposure of a chemoreceptor cell to various different kinds of chemicals results in the generation of a nervous impulse for some chemicals, but not for others.   [4 marks]

This page isn't as stimulating as I expected...

You should have some idea now about what receptors do and why they're important. It's basically so that organisms can respond to their environment. Being able to see, hear, feel, smell and taste allows them to find food and shelter, escape predators, avoid injury and illness and find a mate — survive, really.

The Mammalian Eye

For some reason the eye seems more interesting than most of the other subjects in this section. Maybe it's because we're very aware of our own eyes — more so than our muscles or our nerves, anyway.

The **Eye** is an organ with **Photoreceptors** for detecting light

1) The mammalian eye is a fluid-filled ball bound by a tough external **sclera**, which forms the transparent **cornea** in front.

2) A thinner transparent **conjunctiva** covers the cornea.

3) The inner lining of the back of the eyeball is the photoreceptive **retina**.

4) Between the sclera and the retina is the **choroid**, which is a layer rich in blood vessels to supply the retina and covered with pigment cells to prevent internal reflection of light.

5) The shape of the eyeball is maintained by the hydrostatic pressure of the **aqueous humour** behind the cornea (a clear salt solution) and the jelly-like **vitreous humour** behind the lens.

6) Light rays pass through the **pupil** (hole in the front) and are focused by the **lens** onto the **fovea** of the retina.

7) Action potentials are then carried from the retina to the brain by the **optic nerve**, a bundle of sensory neurones.

8) The **blind spot** is where the optic nerve leaves the eye. There are no photoreceptors there so it's **not** light sensitive.

> The **iris** is a muscular diaphragm surrounding the **pupil**. It controls the amount of **light** entering the eye. In bright light the **circular muscle** of the iris **contracts** and the **radial muscle relaxes**, making the pupil **smaller**. Less light enters the eye, preventing **damage** to the **retina**. The opposite happens in dim light — the iris makes the pupil **dilate** to allow more light in.

Light Rays are *Refracted* to focus on the *Retina*

Light rays are **refracted** (bent) as they pass through the **cornea** and the **lens**. Most refraction happens at the cornea, and then the lens **fine-tunes** the direction of the light to focus it onto the **retina**. It does this by changing its **shape** so that the light is refracted more or less. Surrounding the lens is a radial array of **suspensory ligaments** that are connected by a ring of **ciliary muscles**:

1) When the eye focuses on a **distant** object the ciliary muscles **relax**, which pulls the **suspensory ligaments** taut. This pulls the lens **flat**.

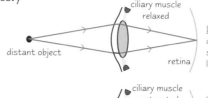

Light from a Distant Object
circular ciliary muscles relaxed;
suspensory ligaments taut;
lens pulls in; light focused on retina.

2) When the eye focuses on a **near** object the ciliary muscles **contract**, so the **suspensory ligaments** are slack. This gives the lens a more **rounded** shape.

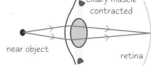

Light from a Near Object
circular ciliary muscles contracted;
suspensory ligaments slack;
elastic lens more convex;
light focused on retina.

The *Retina* is made up of *Three Main Layers*

1) **Photoreceptors** (**rods** and **cones**) which have **outer segments** and **inner segments**:
   - The outer segments have lots of **flattened vesicles** containing **pigments** that absorb light energy. When light is detected, there's a **chemical change** inside the cell which creates a **generator potential** on the cell membrane.
   - The **inner segment** of each receptor has **mitochondria** and a **nucleus**, and connects with a **synapse**.

   Rods and **cones** differ in shape (see diagram). There are **three types** of cones, each with a different type of **pigment**.

2) There's a layer of **bipolar neurones** (with some **cross connections**). The cross connections between the bipolar neurones allow the signals sent from the cells of the retina to be **coordinated**.

3) A layer of **sensory neurones** have axons leading to the **optic nerve**.

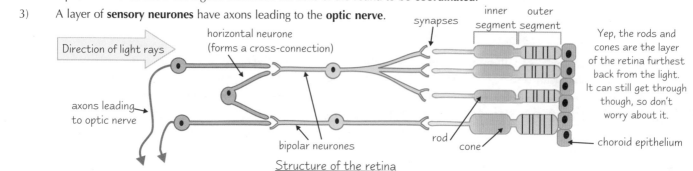

Structure of the retina

The Mammalian Eye

Outer Segments contain Visual Pigments that are Proteins

Rods use a visual pigment called **rhodopsin**. **Cones** use three forms of another pigment called **iodopsin**. This is how **rhodopsin** is used to send impulses to the brain:

1) Light energy is absorbed by a part of the rhodopsin pigment called retinal. This changes shape from one form to another, and detaches from the protein part called opsin. This process is known as bleaching.

2) Bleaching causes an excess of sodium channels to close, so the resting potential value gets more negative (from about -65 mV to about -120 mV).

3) Less inhibitory neurotransmitter is released across the synapse, so there's less inhibition of the bipolar neurone. This means the cell membrane of the bipolar neurone becomes depolarised.

4) An action potential is formed in the bipolar neurone membrane, and is transmitted to the brain through the optic nerve.

Retinal and **opsin** then join back together using an enzyme-catalysed reaction. This **regenerates** the pigment so that it's ready to be stimulated again.
The same sort of thing happens with the **iodopsin** in **cones**, but it breaks apart **less easily** and joins back together **more slowly**. This means that cones are best suited to **higher light intensities**, and we depend more on rods in **dim light**.

Rods are more Sensitive, but Cones let you see more Detail

1) There are about **twenty times** more rods in the human eye than there are cones. The cones are mostly found packed together in the **fovea**, which is where most of the light that enters the eye tends to focus. They give better **visual acuity** (clarity) than rods do, and let us see images more **accurately** and in more **detail**. This is because each cone synapses with its **own individual bipolar synapse**, so it can send more detailed information to the brain. Cones also give **colour vision** (see below).

2) The rods are found outside the fovea, in the more peripheral parts of the retina. They're a lot more **sensitive** than cones, because lots of rods converge onto the **same bipolar neurone**. This means that even **small responses** from many rod cells can be combined and detected in the brain. But having lots of rods converging onto the same bipolar neurone also means that they can't provide as much **clarity** or **detail** as the cones can. This is why an object you can see 'out of the corner of your eye' isn't very clear. You have to move your eyes so that the light from the object focuses on your **fovea** to see it clearly.

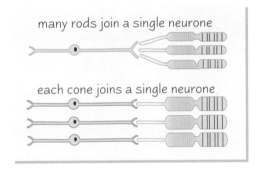
many rods join a single neurone

each cone joins a single neurone

3) Colour vision is explained by the **trichromatic theory**. It states that all the colours we see come from mixing just the **three primary colours** of light — **red**, **blue** and **green**, in different proportions. Each of the three types of **cone** found in the retina is sensitive to **one** of these wavelengths of light. Any particular colour is then experienced because the wavelength stimulates one, two or all three of these types to a different degree.

Practice Questions

Q1 Give the function of the following parts of the eye: a) choroid b) ciliary muscle c) iris.

Q2 What shape is the lens when the eye focuses on a distant object?

Q3 What happens to rhodopsin when it absorbs light energy?

Exam Question

Q1 Explain, with reference to rods and cones, how the human eye has both high sensitivity and high acuity. [8 marks]

Be thankful for the eye — without it, you wouldn't see this lovely page...

OK, so maybe that's not the best reason to be thankful for the eye. In fact, it might be enough to make you wish it had never evolved. But too late, it has, so there's no excuse not to learn about it. Those rod and cone diagrams, the diagram of the eye and those two about the lens have to be learnt. The best way is to practise drawing them yourself.

The ANS and Simple Behaviour Patterns

These pages deal with the autonomic nervous system, which controls all the stuff in your body that happens without you thinking about it. If only revision happened that way...

The **Autonomic Nervous System** controls **Unconscious Activities**

The nervous system is divided into **two parts**:

1) **Conscious activity** is controlled by the **voluntary (somatic) nervous system**.

2) **Unconscious activities**, like the actions of the heart and the digestive system, are controlled by the **autonomic nervous system**, which sends impulses to the involuntary (smooth) muscle and glands. Unconscious, involuntary reactions to stimuli are 'reflex' reactions. They're stereotypic — there's always the same reaction to the stimulus.

The **Autonomic Nervous System** is divided into **Two Parts**

The autonomic nervous system is made up of the **sympathetic** and the **parasympathetic** nervous systems, which have **opposite effects** on organ activity.

These two systems can have **different effects** on the same kinds of muscles because the motor neurones involved secrete different kinds of neurotransmitter at the synapses (see page 71 for more on these). The sympathetic nervous system uses **noradrenaline**, and the parasympathetic system uses **acetylcholine**.

The **Sympathetic** and **Parasympathetic** systems have **Opposite Effects**

The **sympathetic nervous system** is the part of the **autonomic nervous system** that increases the overall physical activity of the body, a response called **'fight or flight'**. In a 'fight or flight' response blood is diverted from the gut to the **lungs**, **heart** and **voluntary muscle**:

1) It **increases** the heart beat rate, to increase **oxygen supply** to the muscles.
2) It **increases** the ventilation rate, so that **more oxygen** can be absorbed in the lungs.
3) It **decreases** peristalsis in the gut so there's more blood available for the heart and lungs.

Other parts of the body also respond to enable **increased sensory awareness**. For example, the radial muscles of the iris contract, causing the pupils of the eye to dilate (see p. 74). The sympathetic nervous system triggers the same kinds of responses as **adrenaline**, the 'fight or flight' **hormone**.

The **parasympathetic nervous system** is the part of the autonomic nervous system that decreases overall physical activity, so it's associated with rest:

1) It **decreases** heart beat rate.
2) It **decreases** ventilation rate.
3) It **increases** peristalsis in the gut, so that food can be digested.

Both **Sympathetic** and **Parasympathetic** Nerves Affect **Heart Beat Rate**

The sympathetic and parasympathetic nervous systems have different effects on heart rate —

1) The brain's **medulla** contains control centres that **increase** activity in the body by sending action potentials along **sympathetic cranial nerves**. They also **decrease** it by sending them along **parasympathetic cranial nerves**.
2) The **sympathetic nerves** secrete a neurotransmitter that **increases** the rate of cardiac muscle **contraction**.
3) The **parasympathetic nerves** secrete a neurotransmitter that **relaxes** muscles and **slows down** the heart beat rate.

The ANS and Simple Behaviour Patterns

Heart Beat is controlled by the ANS

The **sinoatrial node** (SAN) in the heart is connected to both the sympathetic and the parasympathetic nervous systems which speed up and slow down the heart beat rate according to the body's activities.

1) Blood entering the **aorta** stretches the **baroreceptors** in the aorta wall.

2) This causes an action potential to be sent through a **sensory nerve** to the **cardioinhibitory centre** in the **medulla**.

3) The medulla then sends an **impulse** along the motor **vagus** nerve (which is **parasympathetic**) to the **SAN**.

4) The neurotransmitter **acetylcholine** causes the SAN to slow the heart rate.

5) If the heart beats too **slowly**, blood **accumulates** in the **vena cava** putting pressure on the baroreceptors in the vena cava.

6) An **action potential** goes to the **cardioaccelerator centre** of the **medulla**, and then along the motor **accelerator nerve** (which is sympathetic) to the SAN. The neurotransmitter **noradrenaline** is released from the **nerve** and the heart rate increases. This increase in heart rate is called the **Bainbridge Reflex**.

7) Swellings in the carotid arteries of the neck, the **carotid sinuses**, also have **baroreceptors**. They control the **pressure** of blood flowing to the head.

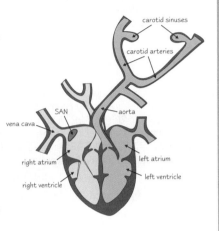
The heart, carotid arteries and carotid sinuses

Taxes and kineses are types of Innate Behaviour

Taxes and kineses are innate (i.e. genetic, not learnt) forms of behaviour that help some organisms to survive.

Taxes

1) A **taxis** is a **directional movement** of the whole organism in response to a **stimulus**.

2) They can be both **negative** (moving away from something) or **positive** (moving towards something).

3) Examples include earthworms — they show **negative phototaxis** (they move away from light) and male moths which show **positive chemotaxis** — they fly towards female moths by detecting the **pheromones** (chemicals) that female moths release into the air.

Kineses

1) A **kinesis** is a change in the rate of movement or activity of an organism, depending on the intensity of a stimulus.

2) For example, **sea anemones** wave their tentacles more when stimulated by **chemicals** emitted by their prey.

You can show the effect of kineses by studying woodlice in a choice chamber. In the light and dry sections they move quickly — this means that they're more likely to move into darker, damper areas where they're less likely to suffer from dehydration. Be careful with this though — the woodlice <u>don't choose</u> where to go, it's just that their innate behaviour means that they're <u>more likely</u> to end up in damper, darker areas.

Practice Questions

Q1 Distinguish between the autonomic and voluntary (somatic) nervous system.
Q2 What is meant by the 'fight or flight' response?
Q3 Give three effects of stimulation of the body by the parasympathetic nervous system.
Q4 What is the difference between taxes and kineses?

Exam Question

Q1 a) Dilation of the vena cava causes the heart rate to increase. Explain how this process happens, paying particular attention to the role of the autonomic nervous system. [6 marks]

b) What would be the effect of severing the nerves from the medulla to the SAN? Explain your answer. [3 marks]

<u>No one will be sympathetic if you don't learn this...</u>

*They're weird names, really. How can a nervous system be sympathetic? It doesn't offer you a tissue when you're upset. Basically, you just have to learn that the sympathetic system gets things ready for fight or flight, and the parasympathetic system calms things down. Try remembering it like this — **s**ympathetic for **s**tress, and **p**arasympathetic for **p**eace.*

Answers

Section 1 — Inheritance and Evolution

Page 3 — Meiosis

1   Maximum of 2 marks available.
    Ovaries **[1 mark]** and testes **[1 mark]**.

2   Maximum of 4 marks available.
    a) A gene is a section of DNA that controls one characteristic /
    controls the synthesis of one or more polypeptide(s) **[1 mark]**.
    An allele is one of the alternative forms of a gene **[1 mark]**.
    b) Haploid cells have half the number of chromosomes as a normal
    cell **[1 mark]**, diploid cells have the full number of chromosomes
    — in pairs of homologous chromosomes **[1 mark]**.

3   Maximum of 3 marks available from the following:
    Meiosis halves the chromosome number **[1 mark]**, so it
    compensates for the doubling of chromosome number at
    fertilisation / maintains the species chromosome number
    [1 mark]. Meiosis also increases variety by producing new
    combinations of alleles **[1 mark]**.

Page 5 — Monohybrid and Dihybrid Crosses

1   Maximum of 3 marks available.
    Carry out a test cross **[1 mark]**, by crossing with a white-flowered
    plant **[1 mark]**. If some of the offspring are white-flowered then
    the plant was heterozygous / If all purple-flowered then the plant
    was homozygous **[1 mark]**.

    *This is a really common question in exams, so make sure you
    answered it correctly.*

Page 7 — Multiple Alleles and Codominance

1   Maximum of 3 marks available — 1 mark for every two correct
    answers from the following.
    $I^A I^A$, $I^A I^O$, $I^B I^B$, $I^B I^O$, $I^A I^B$, $I^O I^O$.

2   Maximum of 2 marks available.
    Conduct a chi-squared test comparing the numbers of people
    with sickle-cell anaemia in places X and Y **[1 mark]**. Use a
    chi-squared table of results to see if the difference between the
    two places is significant, or if it is due to chance **[1 mark]**.

Page 9 — Causes of Variation

1   Maximum of 2 marks available.
    2^3 or $2 \times 2 \times 2$ **[1 mark]**, so 8 possibilities **[1 mark]**.

    In a question like this, always show your working.

2   a) Characteristics that show continuous variation are more likely to
    be affected by the environment **[1 mark]**.
    b) Characteristics that show continuous variation usually involve
    more genes **[1 mark]**.

Page 11 — Investigating Variation

1   a) The curve is bell-shaped **[1 mark]**.
    b) **[1 mark]**

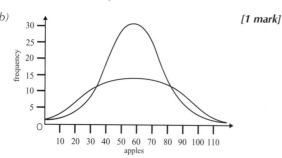

This question is quite hard so don't worry if you got the graph
wrong. You need to realise two things before you can draw the
line: Firstly, when the standard deviation is larger, there are
fewer observations near to the mean, so the peak of the curve
isn't as high as it is for the normal distribution. Secondly, the
observations are more spread out, so there are more
observations nearer the extremes, making the curve fall away
less quickly at the edges.
    c) Maximum of 2 marks available.
    A greater percentage of the trees of the new species will produce
    a quantity of fruit near to the mean **[1 mark]**. This is
    advantageous for farmers because they are more likely to be able
    to predict how big their crop will be with the new species than
    with the one on the graph **[1 mark]**.

Page 13 — Mutation and Phenotype

1   Maximum of 4 marks available.
    Three nucleotides code for a single amino acid **[1 mark]**. If a
    whole amino acid is lost the protein / phenotype is not too badly
    affected **[1 mark]**. If one nucleotide is lost a frame shift **[1 mark]**
    will cause all the amino acids to change and the protein /
    phenotype will be severely affected **[1 mark]**.

2   a) Maximum of 2 marks available.
    To reduce the radiographer's exposure to X-rays **[1 mark]**.
    X-rays are mutagenic / carcinogenic **[1 mark]**.
    b) Maximum of 2 marks available.
    Sunlight contains UV rays **[1 mark]**, which are mutagenic /
    carcinogenic **[1 mark]**.
    c) Maximum of 2 marks available.
    The X-rays increase the frequency of mutation in the parent flies'
    sex cells / gametes **[1 mark]**. This leads to the production of
    genetic abnormalities in the next generation **[1 mark]**.

Page 15 — Frequency of Alleles

1   Maximum of 4 marks available.
    p = frequency of allele M,   q = frequency of allele N.
    The frequency of genotype MM = 0.36
    Therefore, $p^2 = 0.36$, and $p = 0.60$ **[1 mark]**
    So, $q = 1-0.60 = 0.40$ **[1 mark]**
    Frequency of blood group MN = $2pq = 2 \times 0.6 \times 0.4 = 0.48$
    [1 mark]. Frequency of blood group N = $q^2 = 0.4^2 = 0.16$
    [1 mark].

2   Maximum of 4 marks available.
    Frequency of the sickle-cell allele would decrease **[1 mark]**,
    because it now gives a disadvantage / no longer has any
    advantage **[1 mark]**. Frequency of the normal allele would
    increase **[1 mark]**. These changes are caused by directional
    selection **[1 mark]**.

Page 17 — Speciation

1   a) Maximum of 3 marks available.
    Darwin noticed that there were 14 different species of finch on
    the Galápagos islands **[1 mark]**. Each of these finches occupies a
    different ecological niche **[1 mark]**. The finches have different
    beaks which are adapted to eating different foods **[1 mark]**.
    b) Maximum of 4 marks available.
    Darwin thought that all the finches were originally one species
    living on one island competing for resources **[1 mark]**. Some
    finches flew to other islands and established separate populations
    [1 mark]. Adaptation to different habitat / food sources gradually
    changed the beak shapes of the finches **[1 mark]**. This eventually
    led to the formation of new species **[1 mark]**.

Answers

Page 19 — Classification and Taxonomy

1 Maximum of 2 marks available.
Traditional classification deals with features that are easy to observe *[1 mark]* whilst phylogeny deals with the genetic relationships between organisms *[1 mark]*.

2 Maximum of 5 marks available.
a) phylum *[1 mark]*, b) class *[1 mark]*, c) family *[1 mark]*,
d) Aptenodytes *[1 mark]*, e) patagonicus *[1 mark]*.

You will be given all the information you need for this type of question – you don't need to remember scientific names of organisms but you will need to know the groups in the taxonomic system.

Section 2 — Ecosystems

Page 21 — Energy Transfer in Ecosystems

1 Maximum of 4 marks available.
A habitat is the place where an organism or group of organisms live *[1 mark]*. An ecosystem is not just the place, it also includes other abiotic factors *[1 mark]* such as temperature, oxygen level, soil pH, exposure to wind, etc. *[1 mark for a relevant example]* and biotic factors/living things/communities that live there *[1 mark]*.

2 Maximum of 4 marks available.
Pyramids of number can go out of shape when a single large organism can feed many smaller organisms *[1 mark]*. Pyramids of biomass can go out of shape if you have a population of short-lived and rapidly reproducing organisms *[1 mark]*. Pyramids of energy can never be out of shape because, due to energy wastage between trophic levels *[1 mark]*, there always has to be more energy in the population being fed on than the population feeding on it *[1 mark]*.

Page 23 — Carbon and Nitrogen Cycles

1 Maximum of 10 marks available.
Carbon dioxide is removed from the atmosphere by photosynthesis *[1 mark]*. Carbon dioxide is returned to the atmosphere by respiration *[1 mark]*. Carbon dioxide not released by respiration is released when the organism dies *[1 mark]* by the respiration of decomposers *[1 mark]*. If organisms do not decay, their carbon is not released *[1 mark]*. This carbon can eventually form fossil fuels *[1 mark]*. Humans burn large quantities of fossil fuels *[1 mark]* which releases a lot of carbon dioxide *[1 mark]*. Deforestation can also raise carbon dioxide levels *[1 mark]* by killing trees that would absorb it *[1 mark]*.

Page 25 — Investigating Numbers and Distribution

1 Maximum of 3 marks available.
The light meter would take a measurement for one moment in time *[1 mark]* but light intensity changes over time *[1 mark]*. A single reading would not take these variations into account and would therefore not give an accurate representation of the genuine amount of light in the area *[1 mark]*.

2 Maximum of 2 marks available.
A transect would be used to discover a trend across an ecosystem *[1 mark]*. Any suitable example (e.g. distribution of organisms up a rocky shore, distribution of plants with increasing shade) *[1 mark]*.

3 Maximum of 2 marks available.
Population size = $n_1 \times n_2 / n_m$, 80 x 100/10 = 800
[2 marks for correct answer or 1 mark for correct working].

Page 27 — Diversity

1 Maximum of 5 marks available from any of the following:
Stability means that an ecosystem is more resistant to change and/or more likely to recover from damage *[1 mark]*. High diversity leads to high stability *[1 mark]*. High diversity means a large number of species *[1 mark]*. Food webs are more complex where diversity is high *[1 mark]*. There are more potential sources of food for animals where there is high diversity *[1 mark]*. If a species is severely reduced or wiped out, its predators are less likely to be severely affected *[1 mark]* and the effect on the ecosystem will be less *[1 mark]*.
Most of the above points refer to high diversity ecosystems. The marks can also be gained by making the opposite points about low diversity ecosystems.

2 Maximum of 8 marks available.
Map the field *[1 mark]*. Divide it into numbered squares *[1 mark]*. Use a random sampling technique to select the squares to sample *[1 mark]*. Place quadrats in the selected squares *[1 mark]*. Quadrats should be divided into 100 smaller squares *[1 mark]*. Count the number of squares of clover *[1 mark]*. Count only squares which are at least half occupied by clover *[1 mark]*. Average the count for all the quadrats used OR add the total number of squares covered in all the quadrats and convert to a percentage of the total number of squares sampled *[1 mark]*.

Page 29 — Succession

1 Maximum of 8 marks available.
Succession is a process where plant communities gradually develop on bare land *[1 mark]*. Change goes through stages called seral stages *[1 mark]*. The process stops when a climax community is reached *[1 mark]*. Changes are brought about by the interactions of species *[1 mark]*. Climax may be climatic *[1 mark]* resulting from the climate *[1 mark]* or a plagioclimax *[1 mark]* resulting from human activity *[1 mark]*.

2 a) Maximum of 3 marks available from the points below:
Successful features — rapid growth *[1 mark]*, rapid reproduction *[1 mark]*, asexual reproduction *[1 mark]*, efficient seed dispersal *[1 mark]*, tolerant of harsh environmental conditions e.g. high salt levels and strong winds *[1 mark]*.
b) Maximum of 2 marks available from the points below:
Reasons for disappearance — shaded by larger plants *[1 mark]*, eaten by herbivores *[1 mark]*, unable to compete for water or minerals with newly arrived species *[1 mark]*.

Page 31 — Deforestation

1 Maximum of 4 marks available for any of the following.
Growing fast-growing trees *[1 mark]* which will replace themselves quickly *[1 mark]*. Coppicing or pollarding *[1 mark]* which allows timber to be removed repeatedly without killing the tree *[1 mark]*, increases species diversity *[1 mark]* and allows light to reach the floor level *[1 mark]*.

Answers

Section 3 — Energy Processes

Page 33 — Energy Supply and the Role of ATP

1   Maximum of 2 marks available.
ATP is a molecule made from adenosine diphosphate (ADP) and phosphate, using energy from reactions like those of respiration *[1 mark]*. The energy stored in the chemical bond between the ADP and the phosphate can be released when it is needed by a cell, by breaking the ATP back down into ADP and phosphate *[1 mark]*.

2   Maximum of 3 marks available.
Because ATP is small and water-soluble, it can be easily transported around a cell or between cells to the places where there is a demand for energy *[1 mark]*. There it can be rapidly converted back into ADP to release the energy stored in the bonds *[1 mark]*. Because an enzyme is required for this reaction, there is little risk of the ATP breaking down into ADP and releasing its energy in the wrong place, wasting the energy *[1 mark]*.

Page 35 — Glycolysis and the Link Reaction

1   Maximum of 5 marks available.
The 6-carbon glucose molecule is hydrolysed / split using water *[1 mark]*, and phosphorylated using phosphate from 2 molecules of ATP *[1 mark]* to give 2 molecules of a triose phosphate *[1 mark]*. This is then oxidised by removing hydrogen ions *[1 mark]* to give 2 molecules of 3-carbon pyruvate *[1 mark]*.

2   Maximum of 4 marks available.
The 3-carbon pyruvate is combined with coenzyme A *[1 mark]* to form a 2-carbon molecule, acetyl coenzyme A *[1 mark]*. The extra carbon is released as carbon dioxide *[1 mark]*. The coenzyme NAD is converted into reduced NAD in this reaction by accepting hydrogen ions *[1 mark]*.

You need to know how many carbons there are in each molecule. That decides the molecule's basic structure, and it's the most important change from molecule to molecule in these big chains you have to know about. Learn the names of the molecules by all means, but if you forget one in the exam and just put '3-carbon compound', I bet you get the marks.

Page 37 — The Krebs Cycle

1   Maximum of 14 marks available.
1 mark can be awarded for any of the following points, even if the final answer is incorrect:
2 ATP are produced in glycolysis *[1 mark]*. 1 ATP is produced per turn of the Krebs cycle *[1 mark]*, which happens twice per molecule of glucose *[1 mark]* giving 2 ATP from the Krebs cycle per molecule of glucose *[1 mark]*.
In the electron transport chain, 2.5 ATP are produced for every molecule of reduced NAD coenzyme made in the earlier stages of respiration *[1 mark]*, and 1.5 ATP for every molecule of reduced FAD produced *[1 mark]*.
2 reduced NAD are produced in glycolysis *[1 mark]*, 1 reduced NAD is produced in the link reaction *[1 mark]* and 3 in the Krebs cycle *[1 mark]*, but for every molecule of glucose, 2 molecules of pyruvate are made by glycolysis *[1 mark]*, so the link reaction and Krebs cycle happen twice per molecule of glucose *[1 mark]*.
So in total, 8 molecules of reduced NAD are produced by the link reaction and the Krebs cycle *[1 mark]*. Adding the 2 reduced NAD produced in glycolysis gives 10 molecules of reduced NAD *[1 mark]*. $10 \times 2.5 = 25$ ATP *[1 mark]*.
1 molecule of reduced FAD is also produced per turn of the Krebs cycle *[1 mark]*, giving 2 reduced FAD per glucose molecule *[1 mark]*. $2 \times 1.5 = 3$ATP *[1 mark]*.
So in total, the electron transport chain produces $25 + 3 = 28$ ATP *[1 mark]*.
Adding the ATP produced in glycolysis and in the Krebs cycle gives $28 + 2 + 2 = 32$ molecules of ATP in total *[1 mark]*.

Page 39 — The Biochemistry of Respiration

1 a) Maximum of 10 marks available from the following points:
The two forms of anaerobic respiration are alcohol fermentation and the lactate fermentation *[1 mark]*.
Both are ways of releasing energy without using oxygen *[1 mark]*, and both take place in the cytoplasm rather than in mitochondria *[1 mark]*. Both produce 2 ATP per molecule of glucose *[1 mark]*, and both begin by using the process of glycolysis *[1 mark]* to convert glucose into 2 molecules of pyruvate *[1 mark]*.
They differ in what happens next — in alcohol fermentation, carbon dioxide is removed from the pyruvate to give 2-carbon acetaldehyde *[1 mark]*. A molecule of reduced NAD from glycolysis is then oxidised back to NAD *[1 mark]*, and the hydrogen ions it gives up are transferred to the acetaldehyde, making ethanol (alcohol) *[1 mark]*.
In lactate fermentation, no carbon dioxide is given off *[1 mark]* — reduced NAD is used to supply the hydrogen ions needed to reduce the pyruvate to lactic acid/lactate *[1 mark]*.
Alcohol fermentation happens in plants and some micro-organisms, and lactate fermentation happens in animals *[1 mark]*.

b) Maximum of 3 marks available.
Aerobic respiration produces 32 molecules of ATP per molecule of glucose *[1 mark]*, and anaerobic respiration produces only 2 molecules of ATP per molecule of glucose *[1 mark]*. So in terms of ATP production, aerobic respiration is 16 times more efficient than anaerobic respiration *[1 mark]*.

Answers

2 Maximum of 2 marks available.

$$RQ = \frac{CO_2}{O_2} = \frac{102}{145} = 0.7$$

[1 mark for the showing the working, 1 mark for correct answer]

Try to find an easy way to remember that CO_2 goes on top of O_2 in the RQ equation — alphabetical order, perhaps? Two easy marks if you can remember it.

Page 41 — The Biochemistry of Photosynthesis

1 a) In the thylakoid membranes of the chloroplasts **[1 mark]**.
 b) Maximum of 2 marks available.
   ATP **[1 mark]** and NADPH + H⁺ / reduced NADP / NADPH **[1 mark]**.
 c) Maximum of 3 marks available.
   ATP is produced by both cyclic **[1 mark]** and non-cyclic photophosphorylation **[1 mark]**. NADPH is produced by non-cyclic photophosphorylation **[1 mark]**.

Page 43 — The Biochemistry of Photosynthesis

1 Maximum of 5 marks available.
 a) Ribulose bisphosphate (RuBP) **[1 mark]**.
 b) NADPH/reduced NADP **[1 mark]**.
 c) Ribulose bisphosphate (RuBP) **[1 mark]**.
 d) the enzyme ribulose bisphosphate carboxylase **[1 mark]**.
 e) Ribulose bisphosphate (RuBP) **[1 mark]**.

2 Maximum of 3 marks available.
 a) Between points a and b, light was available and both stages of photosynthesis (light-dependent and light-independent) were happening. ATP and NADPH/reduced NADP were being supplied for the Calvin cycle **[1 mark]**.
 b) At point b the light faded and the light-dependent stage of photosynthesis stopped, but the light-independent stage / Calvin cycle continued until point c **[1 mark]**.
 c) Photosynthesis stopped at c as supplies of ATP and NADPH were exhausted and no more could be produced **[1 mark]**.

Section Four — Physiological Control

Page 45 — Water Uptake in Plants

1 Maximum of 4 marks available:
   Loss of water from the leaves due to transpiration pulls more water in from xylem **[1 mark]**.
   There are cohesive forces between water molecules **[1 mark]**. These cause water to be pulled up the xylem **[1 mark]**.
   Removing leaves means no transpiration occurs, so no water is pulled up the xylem **[1 mark]**.

   It's pretty obvious (because there are 4 marks to get) that it's not enough just to say removing the leaves stops transpiration. You also need to explain why transpiration is so important in moving water through the xylem. It's always worth checking how many marks a question is worth — this gives you a clue about how long your answer should be and the level of detail you need to give.

Page 47 — Homeostasis and Temperature Control

1 a) Maximum of 2 marks available.
   A change in a factor brings about a response that counteracts the change / makes it opposite **[1 mark]** so that the factor returns to a norm **[1 mark]**.
 b) Maximum of 2 marks available from any of the following.
   Body temperature **[1 mark]**, blood glucose concentration **[1 mark]**, water potential **[1 mark]**. Or other sensible answer.

2 Maximum of 6 marks available from any of the following.
   More food is consumed by the mouse because the mouse is an endotherm and the lizard is an ectotherm **[1 mark]**. The mouse has a higher metabolic / respiratory rate **[1 mark]** in order to generate more body heat **[1 mark]**, so more food / glucose / carbohydrate is needed as a source of energy **[1 mark]**. The rate is temperature dependent in the lizard because the increase in external temperature raises the body temperature of the lizard, but not of the mouse **[1 mark]**. The lizard's metabolic / respiratory rate increases **[1 mark]** so its energy demand increases **[1 mark]**.

Page 49 — Blood Glucose Control

1 a) Maximum of 10 marks available from the following.
   Glucose is absorbed into the blood (from the gut) **[1 mark]** which makes the blood glucose concentration increase **[1 mark]**. This stimulates the beta cells **[1 mark]** of the islets of Langerhans **[1 mark]** to secrete insulin **[1 mark]**. Insulin is released into the bloodstream **[1 mark]** and binds to receptors **[1 mark]** on liver cells **[1 mark]**. This increases the permeability of the liver cells to glucose **[1 mark]**, converting glucose into glycogen / stimulating glycogenesis **[1 mark]**. This reduces blood glucose concentration **[1 mark]**.
 b) Maximum of 2 marks available.
   There are no / insufficient receptors for insulin **[1 mark]** so insulin can't bind to / stimulate the liver cells **[1 mark]**.

2 Maximum of 5 marks available.
   Exercise uses up glucose (by respiration) **[1 mark]** which lowers blood glucose concentration **[1 mark]** and stimulates the alpha cells **[1 mark]** of the islets of Langerhans **[1 mark]** to secrete glucagon **[1 mark]**.

Page 51 — Methods of Removing Nitrogenous Waste

1 a) Maximum of 6 marks available from the following:
   Protein in food is digested / hydrolysed in the gut / stomach / (small) intestine **[1 mark]** into amino acids **[1 mark]**. If a lot of protein is digested, excess amino acids will be deaminated / have amino groups removed **[1 mark]** in the liver **[1 mark]** to form ammonia **[1 mark]**. The ammonia reacts with carbon dioxide **[1 mark]** to form urea **[1 mark]**, and more urea is excreted in the urine by the kidneys **[1 mark]**.

   It's important to say that only the <u>excess</u> amino acids are deaminated.

2 Maximum of 4 marks available.
   Ammonia is very soluble / more soluble than urea **[1 mark]**, so it can diffuse into the surrounding water **[1 mark]**. This means that conversion to urea isn't needed **[1 mark]**, and so less energy is needed / used **[1 mark]**.

Page 53 — Kidney Function

1 a) Maximum of 5 marks available.
   Microvilli provide a large surface area of membrane **[1 mark]** so there is a large surface area available for substances to pass across and more carrier proteins **[1 mark]**. There are lots of mitochondria **[1 mark]** which provide energy / ATP for reabsorption **[1 mark]** by active transport **[1 mark]**.
 b) Maximum of 3 marks available from the following:
   More glucose passes into the blood, because it is actively reabsorbed **[1 mark]**, but there is no carrier protein for urea **[1 mark]**. Some urea passes into the blood by diffusion **[1 mark]** because it's a small molecule **[1 mark]**.

Answers

2   Maximum of 2 marks available.
    Either blood pressure is high(er) **[1 mark]**; so proteins get filtered out of blood **[1 mark]**. **Or** the wall of the capillary / basement membrane / wall of renal capsule is damaged / more perforated **[1 mark]** so that larger molecules are being filtered out **[1 mark]**.

Page 55 — Water Balance

1   Maximum of 10 marks available.
    Strenuous exercise causes more sweating **[1 mark]** so more water is lost from the body **[1 mark]**. This increases the blood solute concentration / decreases blood water potential / makes blood water potential more negative **[1 mark]**. It also stimulates osmoreceptors **[1 mark]** in the hypothalamus **[1 mark]**, which stimulates the pituitary gland **[1 mark]** to release **more** ADH **[1 mark]**.

    The answer up to this point has explained the cause of the increase in level of ADH in the blood. After this, the answer explains the effect on the kidney.

    ADH increases the permeability of the collecting ducts **[1 mark]** so more water is reabsorbed into the blood by osmosis **[1 mark]**. This means that less water is lost in the urine which prevents further dehydration **[1 mark]**.

2   Maximum of 5 marks available.
    More sodium chloride is removed from the ascending limb **[1 mark]** of a longer loop by active transport **[1 mark]** so solute concentration rises / solute potential falls / water potential falls / becomes more negative in the medulla **[1 mark]**; so **more** water is reabsorbed from the collecting duct **[1 mark]** by osmosis **[1 mark]**.

Page 57 — Gas Exchange Surfaces

1   Maximum of 3 marks available.
    a) High **[1 mark]**.
    b) High **[1 mark]**.
    c) Low **[1 mark]**.

    Examiners like to ask questions where you can apply your knowledge. This question is actually fairly simple. It's just getting you to think about the adaptations that organisms have to make gaseous exchange as efficient as possible.

Page 59 — Transport of Respiratory Gases

1   Maximum of 2 marks available.

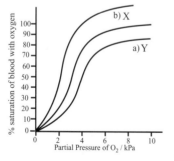

Section 5 — Digestion and Absorption

Page 61 — Digestion and Absorption

1   Maximum of 6 marks available for any 6 of the following:
    The gut wall has a single layer of epithelial cells so there's a short diffusion pathway **[1 mark]**. The lining is moist which aids diffusion **[1 mark]**. There is a good blood supply with lots of capillaries to take away dissolved nutrients and maintain a high concentration gradient **[1 mark]**. Carrier proteins in the membranes allow facilitated diffusion **[1 mark]**. The small intestine has lots of villi and microvilli which provide a large surface area for absorption **[1 mark]**. It has several muscular layers which allow food to be moved along via peristalsis **[1 mark]**. There are lots of mitochondria to make the ATP needed for the active transport of digested material **[1 mark]**. The gut wall has good connections to the lymphatic system so that fatty acids and glycerol can be removed **[1 mark]**.

Page 63 — Digestion and Absorption

1   Maximum of 4 marks available, from any of the 8 points below.
    Polypeptides are broken down by peptidases **[1 mark]** to form amino acids **[1 mark]** when peptide bonds are hydrolysed **[1 mark]**. Exopeptidases hydrolyse peptide bonds between amino acids on the outside **[1 mark]** of the polypeptide chain. Endopeptidases hydrolyse peptide bonds between amino acids on the inside **[1 mark]** of the polypeptide chain. Peptidases are released into the acidic conditions of the stomach in gastric juice **[1 mark]** and in the duodenum from pancreatic juice **[1 mark]** and from the epithelial cells lining the small intestine **[1 mark]**.

2   Maximum of 6 marks available from the following:
    Amylase is used to hydrolyse starch to maltose **[1 mark]**. Maltase is used to hydrolyse maltose to glucose **[1 mark]**. Pepsin is used to hydrolyse protein to polypeptides **[1 mark]**. Trypsin is also used to hydrolyse protein into polypeptides **[1 mark]**. Chymotrypsin hydrolyses proteins into polypeptides **[1 mark]**. Lipase hydrolyses fats into fatty acids and glycerol **[1 mark]**. Exopeptidases hydrolyse the peptide bonds found at the end of polypeptide chains **[1 mark]**. Endopeptidases break the bonds in the middle of polypeptide chains **[1 mark]**. Dipeptidases break short polypeptide chains into single amino acids **[1 mark]**.

    Remember — bile salts emulsify fats to fatty droplets but they aren't enzymes.

Page 65 — Control of Digestive Secretions

1   Maximum of 5 marks available.
    Reflex reactions produce saliva **[1 mark]** and gastric juices **[1 mark]**. Acetylcholine increases the muscle action in the stomach and intestines **[1 mark]**. Extrinsic nerves cause the release of adrenaline which inhibits the digestive system muscles **[1 mark]**. Nervous impulses from the autonomic nervous system control peristalsis **[1 mark]**.

2   Maximum of 3 marks available.
    a) Nervous or hormonal **[1 mark]**.
    b) Nervous reflex **[1 mark]**.
    c) Hormonal **[1 mark]**.

Page 67 — Metamorphosis and Insect Diet

1   Maximum of 6 marks available.
    Egg — peptidases, lipase **[2 marks]**, Caterpillar — peptidases, cellulase, and amylase **[3 marks]**. (Pupa — none) Butterfly — sucrase **[1 mark]**.

    Make sure you know the enzymes relating to each stage of the insect's life — it comes up a lot in exams.

Answers

2   Maximum of 3 marks available.
  a) Mandibles — the strong jaws that caterpillars use to cut through leaves **[1 mark]**.
  b) Imaginal discs — the clusters of cells which trigger the change into specific parts of the adult butterfly during the pupal stage **[1 mark]**.
  c) Maxillae — structures on jaws of the caterpillar which help it to recognise food, and push food into the mouth **[1 mark]**.

Section Six — The Nervous System

Page 69 — Neurones

1 a) Stimulus **[1 mark]**.
  b) Maximum of 3 marks available.
     A stimulus causes sodium channels in the neurone cell membrane to open **[1 mark]**   Sodium diffuses into the cell **[1 mark]**, so the membrane becomes depolarised / more positive charge moves in (than moves out) **[1 mark]**.
  c) Maximum of 2 marks available, from any of the following.
     The membrane was in the refractory period **[1 mark]** and so the sodium channels were inactive / recovering / couldn't be opened **[1 mark]**. Alternatively, the stimulus could have been lower than threshold level **[1 mark]**.

2   Maximum of 5 marks available, for any 5 of the following:
    Transmission of action potentials will be slower **[1 mark]**. Myelin insulates the axon / has high electrical resistance **[1 mark]** and there are gaps / nodes of Ranvier between sheaths **[1 mark]** where depolarisation happens /sodium channels are concentrated **[1 mark]**. So in an intact myelinated axon, saltatory transmission occurs / action potentials jump from node to node **[1 mark]**. This can't happen if the myelin sheath is damaged / more membrane is exposed **[1 mark]**.

    Don't panic if a question mentions something you haven't learned about. You might not know anything about multiple sclerosis, and that's fine because you're not supposed to.
    All you need to know about to get full marks here is the structure of neurones.

Page 71 — Synaptic Transmission

1   Maximum of 8 marks available, for any 8 of the following:
    Arrival of the action potential causes calcium channels to open (in the presynaptic membrane) **[1 mark]** which makes calcium diffuse into the bouton / synaptic knob / cell **[1 mark]**. This stimulates the vesicles in the bouton to fuse with the presynaptic membrane **[1 mark]** and release the neurotransmitter **[1 mark]** by exocytosis **[1 mark]**. The neurotransmitter diffuses across the gap / cleft **[1 mark]** and binds to receptors on the postsynaptic membrane **[1 mark]**   This stimulates opening of sodium channels (on the postsynaptic membrane) **[1 mark]** so sodium diffuses into the cell **[1 mark]**. The membrane then becomes depolarised **[1 mark]**.

2   Maximum of 4 marks available.
    Vesicles (containing neurotransmitter) are only found in the presynaptic neurone **[1 mark]**, so exocytosis / release / secretion (of neurotransmitter) can only happen from here **[1 mark]**. The receptors (for the neurotransmitter) are only found on the postsynaptic membrane **[1 mark]** so only this membrane can be stimulated by the neurotransmitter / neurotransmitter can only bind here **[1 mark]**.

Page 73 — Receptors and the Reflex Arc

1   Maximum of 4 marks available for any of the following points:
    Chemoreceptor cells have membrane-bound receptor molecules / proteins **[1 mark]**. The stimulus molecule must have a complementary shape **[1 mark]** to bind to the receptor molecule **[1 mark]** and create a generator potential **[1 mark]** to transmit a nerve impulse **[1 mark]**.

Page 75 — The Mammalian Eye

1   Maximum of 8 marks available.
    Cones are responsible for the high acuity of the human eye **[1 mark]**. They're densely packed at the fovea, where most of the light that enters the eye tends to focus **[1 mark]**. Each synapses with just one bipolar neurone **[1 mark]**, so it can send very detailed information to the brain **[1 mark]**. Rods are found in the more peripheral parts of the retina **[1 mark]**. They're more sensitive than cones, because it takes less light to activate the pigment inside them **[1 mark]**. Lots of rods converge onto the same bipolar neurone too **[1 mark]**, so even if only a few are stimulated by dim light a message is still sent to the brain **[1 mark]**.

Page 77 — The ANS and Simple Behaviour Patterns

1 a) Maximum of 6 marks available from the following:
     Baroreceptors in the wall of the vena cava are stimulated by the increasing blood pressure **[1 mark]**. An action potential / nerve impulse is sent along the sensory nerve/neurone **[1 mark]** to the cardioaccelerator centre **[1 mark]** in the medulla oblongata **[1 mark]**. An action potential / nerve impulse is sent along the motor nerve / neurone **[1 mark]** which is part of the sympathetic nervous system **[1 mark]** to the SAN, where noradrenaline is released which then increases the heart beat rate **[1 mark]**.
  b) Maximum of 3 marks available.
     The heart wouldn't be able to speed up or slow down **[1 mark]** because action potentials / nerve impulses from medulla / cardioaccelerator centre in the medulla would not reach SAN **[1 mark]**. In a normally functioning heart these impulses control heart beat rate **[1 mark]**.

Index

Index

86

Index